VOYAGING

VOYAGING

VOLUME ONE:
THE PLAGUE STAR

GEORGE R. R.
MARTIN

ART AND ADAPTATION BY
RAYA GOLDEN

COLOR ASSISTANCE BY EVAN EVANS
LETTERS BY CARLOS M. MANGUAL

HARPER
Voyager

DEDICATED TO MY MOMMASAN

WANDA JUNE

1951 - 2021

THE PLAGUE STAR TWINKLES BUT LITTLE, SHINING DOWN UPON THE LAND WITH AN ALMOST WHIMSICAL BRIGHTNESS.

WHEN WE FIRST SET DOWN TO WIN OUR FORTUNES, THE PLAGUE STAR WAS ONLY ONE OF MANY SHINING IN THIS STRANGE NIGHT SKY . . . HARD TO EVEN PICK OUT.

IN THAT TIME WE SMILED AT THE SUPERSTITIONS OF THE LOCAL PRIMITIVES, THESE BACKWARD BRUTES WHO THOUGHT SICKNESS COULD COME FROM THE SKY. ≑COFF≑

THEN THE PLAGUE STAR BEGAN TO WAX. NIGHT AFTER NIGHT IT BURNED BRIGHTER . . . ≑COFF-COFF≑

. . . UNTIL IT BECAME VISIBLE EVEN BY DAY. BUT LONG BEFORE THAT, AND UNBEKNOWNST TO US, THE PESTILENCE HAD ALREADY BEGUN.

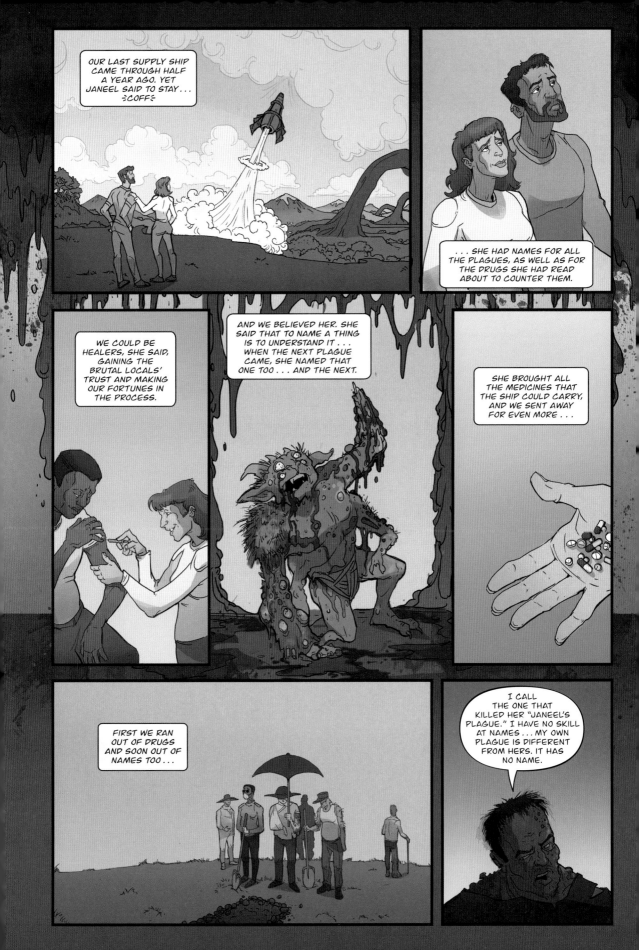

PART ONE: THE CONSPIRACY

--ARE MEANINGLESS! WE HAVE ONE SET OF LAWS HERE ON SHANDELLOR, ANOTHER ON KLERONOMAS, A THIRD ON MAYA, AND NONE OF THEM MEAN A DAMNED THING.

ASSUMING THIS PLAGUE STAR OF YOURS IS REALLY WHAT LEON THINKS IT IS, AND IS STILL IN WORKING ORDER, WHOEVER CONTROLS IT WILL GAIN AN OVERWHELMING MILITARY SUPERIORITY IN THIS SECTOR.

STARSLIP AND OTHER BIG TRANSCORPS ARE AS GREEDY AND RUTHLESS AS I AM. FURTHERMORE, IN CASE IT HAS ESCAPED YOUR NOTICE, THERE ARE ONLY FOUR OF US. FIVE, IF YOU COUNT DAWNSTAR, OUR RESIDENT "HIRELING" OVER THERE. ONCE THEY SEE WHAT WE HAVE, DO YOU IMAGINE FOR EVEN A SECOND THAT WE'D BE ALLOWED TO KEEP IT?

IF THEY CHEAT US, WE'LL SUE THEM.

IN WHAT COURTS? ON WHAT WORLD? YOU'RE ASSUMING WE'LL BE ALLOWED TO LIVE, WHICH IS UNLIKELY. YOU ARE A REMARKABLY STUPID AND UGLY WOMAN.

HERE, HERE! LET'S HAVE NO NAME-CALLING. WE'RE ALL IN THIS TOGETHER, AFTER ALL.

INSULTS ARE USELESS. KAJ NEVIS HAS MADE SOME VALID POINTS. HE IS EXPERIENCED IN THESE AREAS, AND WE ARE NOT.

WHAT IS THE USE OF HAVING BROUGHT HIM INTO THIS AFFAIR IF WE ARE UNWILLING TO LISTEN TO HIS COUNSEL?

YES, RANITTAS IS RIGHT. SO, WHAT DO YOU SUGGEST THEN, NEVIS? IF WE MUST AVOID THE TRANSCORPS, HOW ARE WE TO REACH THE PLAGUE STAR?

THE TRANSCORPS HAVE NO MONOPOLY ON SHIPS. THAT'S WHY I SUGGESTED WE MEET HERE TODAY. THIS DUMP IS CLOSE TO THE PORT.

AND THE MAN WE'RE LOOKING FOR WILL BE HERE SOON. I'M SURE OF IT.

TWO WEEKS LATER...

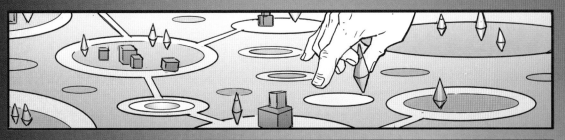

AGAIN.

PERHAPS I MIGHT SUGGEST AN ALTERNATIVE CONTEST?

YEAH, NAH, YOU'RE TOO GOOD AT THESE GAMES. I WAS BORN A GAMBLER, BUT WITH YOU IT'S NO GAMBLE. AND I'M TIRED OF COMING IN SECOND.

UNDOUBTEDLY, MY LUCK WILL HAVE RUN ITS COURSE BY NOW AND YOU WILL OBLITERATE MY POOR FORCES ON YOUR NEXT ATTEMPT.

OH, UNDOUBTEDLY. BUT FORGIVE ME IF I POSTPONE THE ATTEMPT UNTIL THE BOREDOM BECOMES TERMINAL.

AT LEAST I'M BETTER THAN LEON, EH?

THE GAME DOES NOT CONFORM TO AUTHENTIC MILITARY PRINCIPLES, NOR TRIED-AND-TRUE TACTICS.

IT WAS ON MY BED! I WANTED TO TAKE A LITTLE NAP AND THE DAMNED CREATURE WAS ASLEEP ON MY BED!

AND YOU, WIPE THAT SMIRK OFF YOUR FACE. IT'S BAD ENOUGH WE ALL HAVE TO BE COOPED UP TOGETHER IN THIS SHABBY LITTLE SHIP.

I SIMPLY REFUSE TO SHARE WHAT LITTLE SPACE I HAVE WITH THESE VICIOUS PESTS.

EXCUSE ME . . .

. . . IS THIS ONE OF THE VICIOUS PESTS YOU HAD IN MIND?

AND JUST WHAT DO YOU PROPOSE TUF DO WITH OLD MUSHROOM HERE?

PUUUUURRRRRRRR

IT WAS THE OTHER ONE THAT HURT ME, THE BLACK AND WHITE ONE, BUT THAT ONE'S JUST AS BAD. LOOK AT MY FACE! LOOK AT WHAT THEY'VE DONE TO ME.

I CAN SCARCELY BREATHE, I'M BREAKING OUT ALL OVER, AND WHEN I TRY TO SLEEP I WAKE UP WITH ONE OF THEM ON MY CHEST!

YESTERDAY I WAS HAVING A LITTLE SNACK, AND I PUT IT DOWN FOR JUST A MOMENT. WHEN I CAME BACK, THE LITTLE ONE HAD KNOCKED IT OVER AND WAS ROLLING MY SPICED PUFFS AROUND IN THE DIRT LIKE TOYS.

NOTHING IS SAFE AROUND THESE ANIMALS.

I'VE LOST TWO LIGHT PENCILS AND MY BEST PINKY RING. AND NOW THIS?! THIS ATTACK?! THIS IS JUST INTOLERABLE. I MUST INSIST THAT THEY BE PUT DOWN IN THE CARGO HOLD AT ONCE. AT ONCE! DO YOU HEAR?

MY HEARING IS QUITE ADEQUATE, THANK YOU.

AS TO YOUR MISSING PROPERTY...

...IF IT HAS NOT TURNED UP BY THE END OF OUR VOYAGE, I WILL BE MOST PLEASED TO REIMBURSE YOU FOR ITS VALUE.

YOUR REQUEST IN REGARD TO MUSHROOM AND HAVOC, HOWEVER, I MUST REGRETFULLY DENY.

I'M A PASSENGER ON THIS JOKE OF A STARSHIP!

YOUR STATUS AS A PASSENGER HERE IS OBVIOUS. PERMIT ME TO POINT OUT, HOWEVER, THAT THIS SMALL SHIP, WHICH YOU FEEL SO FREE TO INSULT, IS MY HOME.

FURTHERMORE, WHILE YOU ARE UNDENIABLY A PASSENGER HERE AND THEREFORE ENJOY CERTAIN RIGHTS, MUSHROOM AND HAVOC MUST HAVE SUBSTANTIALLY GREATER RIGHTS, SINCE THIS IS THEIR PERMANENT ABODE, SO TO SPEAK.

IT IS NOT MY CUSTOM TO TAKE PASSENGERS ABOARD MY CORNUCOPIA OF EXCELLENT GOODS AT LOW PRICES. REGRETFULLY, I HAVE SUFFERED VARIOUS PROFESSIONAL VICISSITUDES OF LATE.

SO, I MUST BEND ALL MY EFFORTS TO ACCOMMODATE YOU ABOARD THIS CRAFT TO THE EXTENT THAT I HAVE GIVEN OVER MY SHIP'S LIVING QUARTERS TO YOUR COLLECTIVE NEEDS WHILE I MAKE MY OWN POOR BED IN THE CONTROL ROOM.

DESPITE MY UNDENIABLE NEED, I AM NOW COMING TO DEEPLY REGRET THE FOOLISH IMPULSE THAT BID ME TAKE THIS CHARTER. ESPECIALLY AS THE PAYMENT I RECEIVED WAS BARELY SUFFICIENT TO REFUEL AND PROVISION THIS VOYAGE OR PAY MY LANDING TAX FEES.

I HAVE NO DOUBT.

WELL, I NEVER.

I'M NOT GOING TO PUT UP WITH THIS ANY LONGER! THERE'S NO REASON WE ALL HAVE TO BE CRAMMED INSIDE ONE ROOM LIKE SOLDIERS IN BARRACKS. THIS SHIP WASN'T NEARLY THIS SMALL FROM THE OUTSIDE.

WHERE DOES THAT DOOR GO?

TO THE HOLD AND CARGO COMPARTMENTS. THERE ARE SIXTEEN OF THEM. EVEN THE SMALLEST, ADMITTEDLY, HAS TWICE THE SPACE OF MY MEAGER LIVING QUARTERS.

AHA!

AND ARE WE CARRYING ANY CARGO?

COMPARTMENT SIXTEEN IS PACKED WITH PLASTIC REPRODUCTIONS OF COOGISH ORGY-MASKS, AND IN COMPARTMENT TWELVE I STORE CERTAIN PERSONAL EFFECTS, MISCELLANEOUS EQUIPMENT, AND BRIC-A-BRAC.

THE REST OF THE SHIP IS QUITE EMPTY, MADAM.

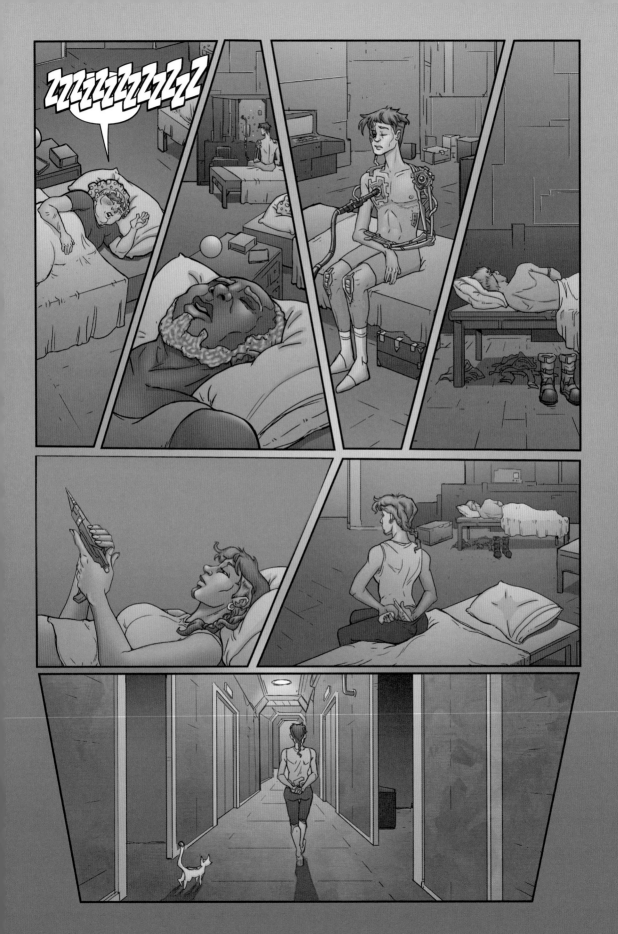

I AM UNFAMILIAR WITH ITS RULES.

OH, THEY'RE SIMPLE ENOUGH.

INDEED. PERHAPS YOU WOULD BE GOOD ENOUGH TO ELABORATE.

YOU WOULD NEVER HAVE WON THE LAST GAME IF PROFESSOR WAN HAD THROWN IN WITH ME WHEN I ASKED HER TO.

ALLIANCES, TUF, CAN BE PROFITABLE TO ALL PARTIES CONCERNED. YOU AND I ARE THE ODD ONES OUT HERE. WE'RE THE HIRELINGS.

IF MISTER "I'M AN OFFICER" JEFRI LEON IS RIGHT ABOUT THE PLAGUE STAR, THE REST OF THEM WILL DIVIDE WEALTH SO VAST IT'S INCOMPREHENSIBLE, WHILE YOU AND I WILL RECEIVE OUR FEES. BIT SUS' INNIT?

EQUITY IS OFTEN DIFFICULT TO JUDGE, AND STILL MORE DIFFICULT TO ACHIEVE.

I MIGHT WISH MY COMPENSATION WERE MORE GENEROUS, BUT IT IS NONETHELESS THE FEE THAT I NEGOTIATED AND ACCEPTED.

NEGOTIATIONS CAN BE REOPENED. THEY NEED US...BOTH OF US. IT OCCURRED TO ME THAT IF WE WORKED TOGETHER, WE MIGHT BE ABLE TO...UH... INSIST UPON BETTER TERMS...

...A FULL SIX-WAY SPLIT, WHAT DO YOU THINK, EH?

AN INTRIGUING NOTION, WITH MUCH TO RECOMMEND IT. SOME MIGHT VENTURE TO SUGGEST THAT IT WAS UNETHICAL, TRUE, BUT THE TRUE SOPHISTICATE RETAINS A CERTAIN MORAL FLEXIBILITY.

YOU DON'T BUY IT, DO YOU, TUF? DOWN DEEP, YOU'RE A STICKLER FOR THE RULES, I CAN TELL.

AN UNPLEASANT SUGGESTION, BUT UNLIKELY ON THE FACE OF IT.

AND SATISFACTION BROUGHT HIM BACK. LEON KNOWS THIS IS ALL WICKED DODGY, AND THEY NEEDED SOME DODGY FOLKS TO GET WHAT THEY WANT OUT OF IT.

THEY HAVE A NICE FOUR-WAY SPLIT SET UP, BUT KAJ HAS THE KIND OF REPUTATION THAT MAKES YOU WONDER IF HE'LL SETTLE FOR A FOURTH. I'M HERE TO SEE THAT HE DOES.

PUUUUURRRRR

BESIDES, I'M INSURANCE AGAINST ANY OTHER COMPLICATIONS THAT MIGHT KICK UP.

HERE'S WHERE I POINT OUT THAT YOU YOURSELF MIGHT CONSTITUTE AN ADDITIONAL COMPLICATION.

IT WAS NOT MY INTENT TO CONVEY SUCH MISINFORMATION, CERTAINLY. I AM NOT AN EATER OF FLESH MYSELF, BUT THERE IS SOME SMALL POOR QUANTITY OF MEAT ABOARD MY MODEST VESSEL. THIS I FREELY ADMIT.

AH, I TOLD YOU HE WAS KEEPING THE GOOD FOOD ALL FOR HIMSELF. NOW THEN, TUF, BRING ME THIS MEAT!

TRUE, THE CONTRACT I MADE WITH KAJ NEVIS REQUIRES ME TO FEED YOU THROUGH THE DURATION OF THIS VOYAGE. NOTHING WAS SAID ABOUT THE NATURE OF THE PROVENDER, HOWEVER. ALWAYS I AM PUT UPON. VERY WELL, SUCH IS MY POOR LOT IN LIFE.

AND YET, NOW I FIND MYSELF TAKEN BY A SUDDEN WHIM OF MY OWN. IF I MUST INDULGE YOUR WHIM, WOULD IT NOT BE EQUITABLE THAT YOU SHOULD SIMILARLY BEND TO MINE?

WHAT DO YOU MEAN?

IT IS NOTHING, REALLY. IN RETURN FOR THE MEAT YOU CRAVE, I ASK ONLY A MOMENT'S INDULGENCE. I HAVE GROWN MOST CURIOUS OF LATE. AWHINA DAWNSTAR HAS WARNED ME THAT, UNSATISFIED, CURIOSITY WILL SURELY KILL MY CATS.

I'M FOR THAT.

INDEED. NONETHELESS, I MUST INSIST. I OFFER YOU A TRADE--FOOD, OF THE TYPE YOU HAVE REQUESTED SO MELODRAMATICALLY, FOR A POOR USELESS NUGGET OF INFORMATION. WE ARE SHORTLY TO ARRIVE IN THE SYSTEM OF HRO B'RANA, YOUR CHARTERED DESTINATION. I WOULD LIKE TO KNOW WHY WE TRAVEL THERE, AND THE NATURE OF WHAT YOU WE EXPECT TO FIND AT THIS PLAGUE STAR OF WHICH I HEARD YOU SPEAK.

THIS IS EXTORTION. JEFRI, PUT YOUR FOOT DOWN.

HEH, WELL, THERE'S REALLY NO HARM, CELISE. HE'LL FIND OUT ANYWAY WHEN WE ARRIVE. PERHAPS IT IS TIME HE KNEW.

PART TWO: THE ARK

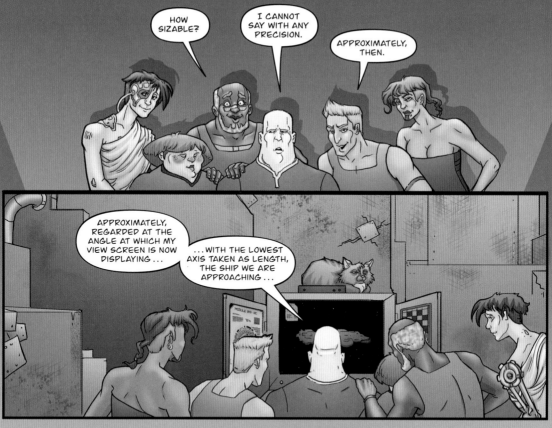

HOW SIZABLE?

I CANNOT SAY WITH ANY PRECISION.

APPROXIMATELY, THEN.

APPROXIMATELY, REGARDED AT THE ANGLE AT WHICH MY VIEW SCREEN IS NOW DISPLAYING...

...WITH THE LOWEST AXIS TAKEN AS LENGTH, THE SHIP WE ARE APPROACHING...

...IT WOULD SEEM TO BE, APPROXIMATELY, SOME THIRTY STANDARD KILOMETERS LONG, APPROXIMATELY FIVE KILOMETERS IN WIDTH, AND APPROXIMATELY THREE KILOMETERS IN HEIGHT.

I WAS RIGHT! IT'S GOT TO BE AN EEC SEEDSHIP. NOTHING ELSE COULD BE SO LARGE!

WE'RE RICH!

WE'RE RICH, RICH, AND *FAMOUS*, WE'RE ALL RICH!

DAMN . . .

THIS IS NOT ENTIRELY CORRECT. WHILE I DO NOT DOUBT THAT YOU MAY INDEED BECOME WEALTHY IN THE NEAR FUTURE, FOR THE MOMENT, HOWEVER, IT WOULD SEEM THAT MISS DAWNSTAR AND I DO NOT SHARE YOUR PROSPECTS OF ECONOMIC ADVANCEMENT.

ARE YOU COMPLAINING, TUF?

FAR BE IT FROM ME TO OBJECT.

I WAS MERELY CORRECTING CELISE WAN'S MISSTATEMENT.

GOOD. NOW, BEFORE ANY OF US GET ANY RICHER, WE HAVE TO GET ABOARD THAT THING AND SEE WHAT SHAPE IT'S IN.

EVEN A DERELICT OUGHT TO NET US A NICE SALVAGE FEE, BUT IF THAT SHIP'S IN WORKING ORDER, THERE'S NO LIMIT TO WHAT WE COULD MAKE.

IT'S OBVIOUSLY FUNCTIONAL. IT HAS BEEN RAINING PLAGUES ON HRO B'RANA EVERY THIRD GENERATION FOR A THOUSAND YEARS.

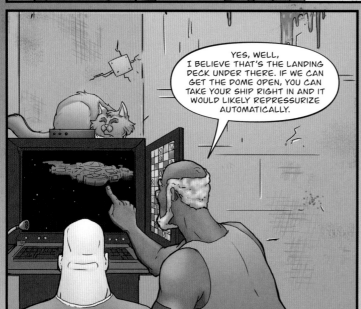

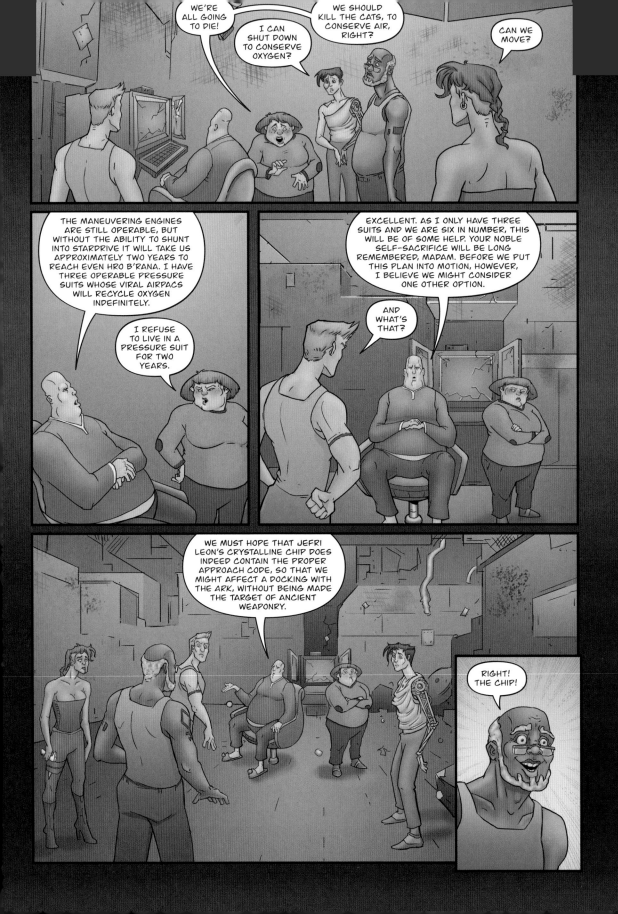

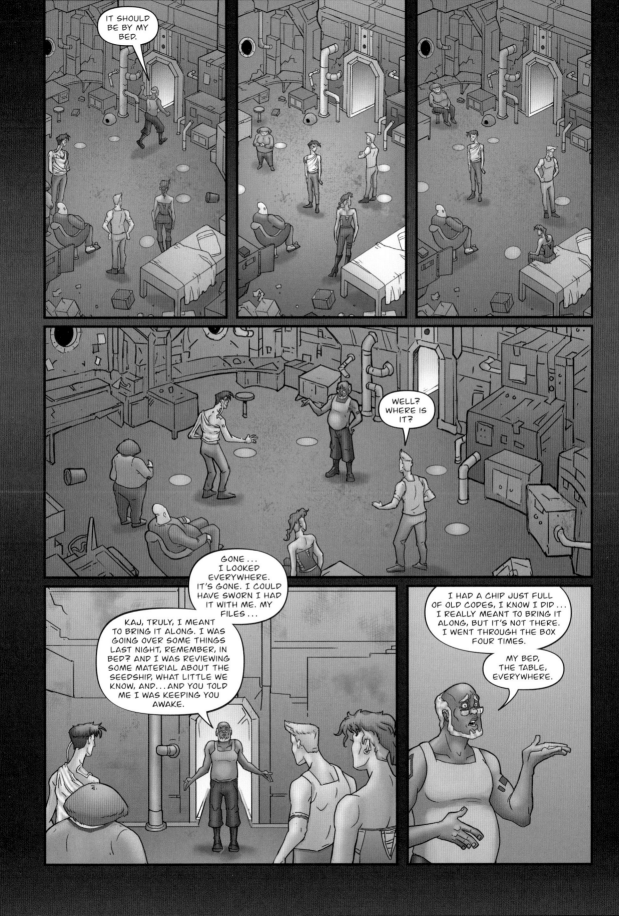

I ... I MUST HAVE LEFT THEM BACK ON SHANDELLOR, WE WERE IN SUCH HASTE TO LEAVE, I--

YOU SENILE OLD FOOL! I OUGHT TO KILL YOU NOW AND SAVE US A LITTLE MORE AIR!

WE'RE DEAD NOW FOR SURE, DEAD, DEAD, DEAD, DEAD!

MADAM, PLEASE, YOU CONTINUE TO BE PREMATURE. YOU ARE NO MORE DECEASED NOW THAN YOU WERE WEALTHY A SHORT TIME AGO.

OH? YOU HAVE AN IDEA, TUF?

DO TELL?

INDEED.

THE ARK IS OUR ONLY SALVATION. WE MUST BOARD HER. WITHOUT JEFRI LEON'S CODE CRYSTAL, WE CANNOT MOVE CLOSER FOR A DOCKING, FOR FEAR OF BEING FIRED UPON ONCE AGAIN. THIS MUCH IS OBVIOUS.

YET AN INTERESTING CONCEPT HAS OCCURRED TO ME. PERHAPS THE ARK MIGHT DISPLAY LESS HOSTILITY TOWARD A SMALLER TARGET-- A MAN IN A PRESSURE SUIT, SAY?

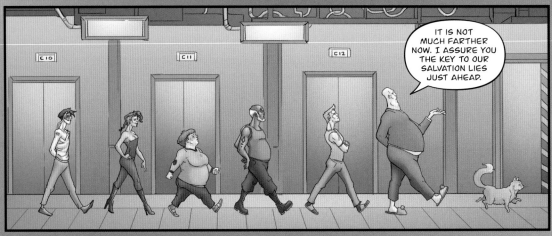

THE ARK IS NOT FIRING ON OUR ERSTWHILE COMPATRIOTS.

THIS IS ALL MY FAULT.

NO. IT'S HIS FAULT!

YOU ARE NOT THE MOST APPRECIATIVE OF WOMEN.

APPRECIATIVE? WHAT AM I SUPPOSED TO APPRECIATE?!

WE ARE NOT WITHOUT RESOURCES. TO BEGIN WITH, KAJ NEVIS HAS LEFT US ONE FUNCTIONAL PRESSURE SUIT.

AND NO PROPULSION SYSTEMS.

OUR AIR WILL LAST TWICE AS LONG WITH OUR NUMBERS DIMINISHED.

BUT IT WILL STILL RUN OUT!

WHAT WE HAVE IS A CRIPPLED SHIP THAT IS RAPIDLY RUNNING OUT OF AIR.

AND FOR THIS I'M TO BE APPRECIA--

WHA--?

OH, IT'S MY GLOWSTONE RING.

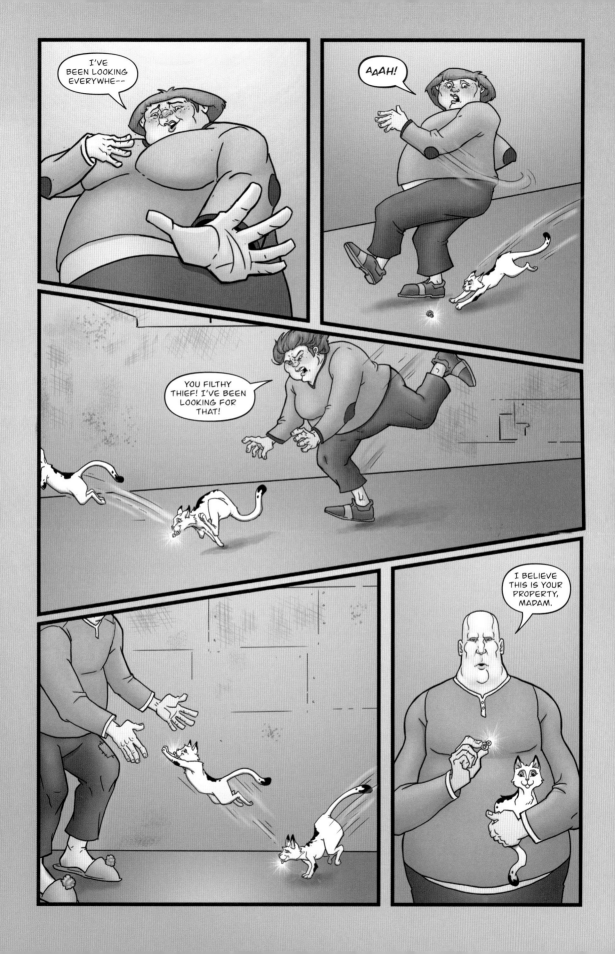

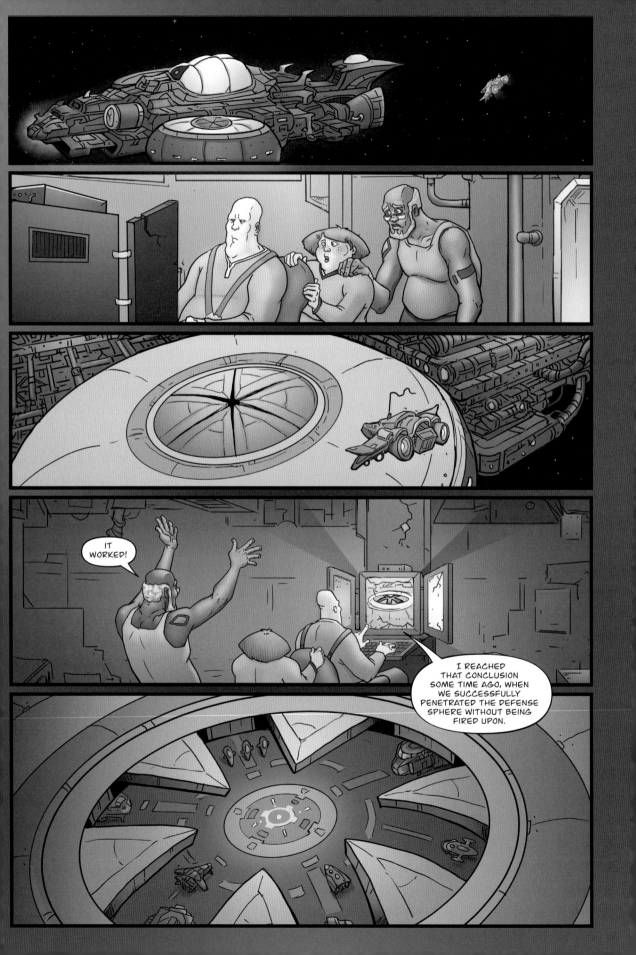

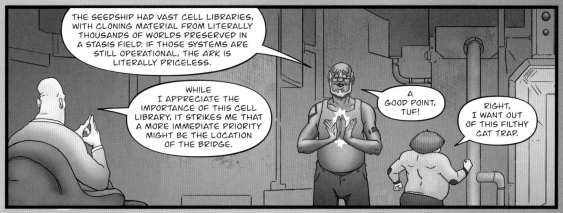

THE SEEDSHIP HAD VAST CELL LIBRARIES, WITH CLONING MATERIAL FROM LITERALLY THOUSANDS OF WORLDS PRESERVED IN A STASIS FIELD. IF THOSE SYSTEMS ARE STILL OPERATIONAL, THE ARK IS LITERALLY PRICELESS.

WHILE I APPRECIATE THE IMPORTANCE OF THIS CELL LIBRARY, IT STRIKES ME THAT A MORE IMMEDIATE PRIORITY MIGHT BE THE LOCATION OF THE BRIDGE.

A GOOD POINT, TUF!

RIGHT, I WANT OUT OF THIS FILTHY CAT TRAP.

A MOMENT, PLEASE. A PROBLEM PRESENTS ITSELF. WE ARE THREE IN NUMBER AND POSSESS ONLY A SINGLE FUNCTIONAL PRESSURE SUIT.

WE'RE INSIDE A SHIP, WHAT DO WE NEED SUITS FOR?

PERHAPS NOTHING. IT US TRUE THE LANDING FIELD SEEMS TO FUNCTION AS A VERY LARGE AIRLOCK WITH AN ENTIRELY BREATHABLE OXYGEN–NITROGEN ATMOSPHERE.

SO WHAT'S THE PROBLEM, TUF?

NO DOUBT I AM BEING OVERCAUTIOUS. I ADMIT TO SOME DISQUIET, HOWEVER.

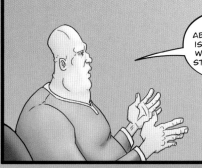

THIS ARK, THOUGH PERHAPS ABANDONED AND DERELICT, IS NONETHELESS DUTIFUL. WITNESS THE PLAGUES IT STILL REGULARLY INFLICTS ON HRO B'RANA.

WITNESS THE EFFICIENCY WITH WHICH IT DEFENDED ITSELF AGAINST APPROACH. PERHAPS THE EXTERNAL DEFENSE SPHERE WAS ONLY THE FIRST OF SEVERAL LINES OF AUTOMATIC DEFENSE.

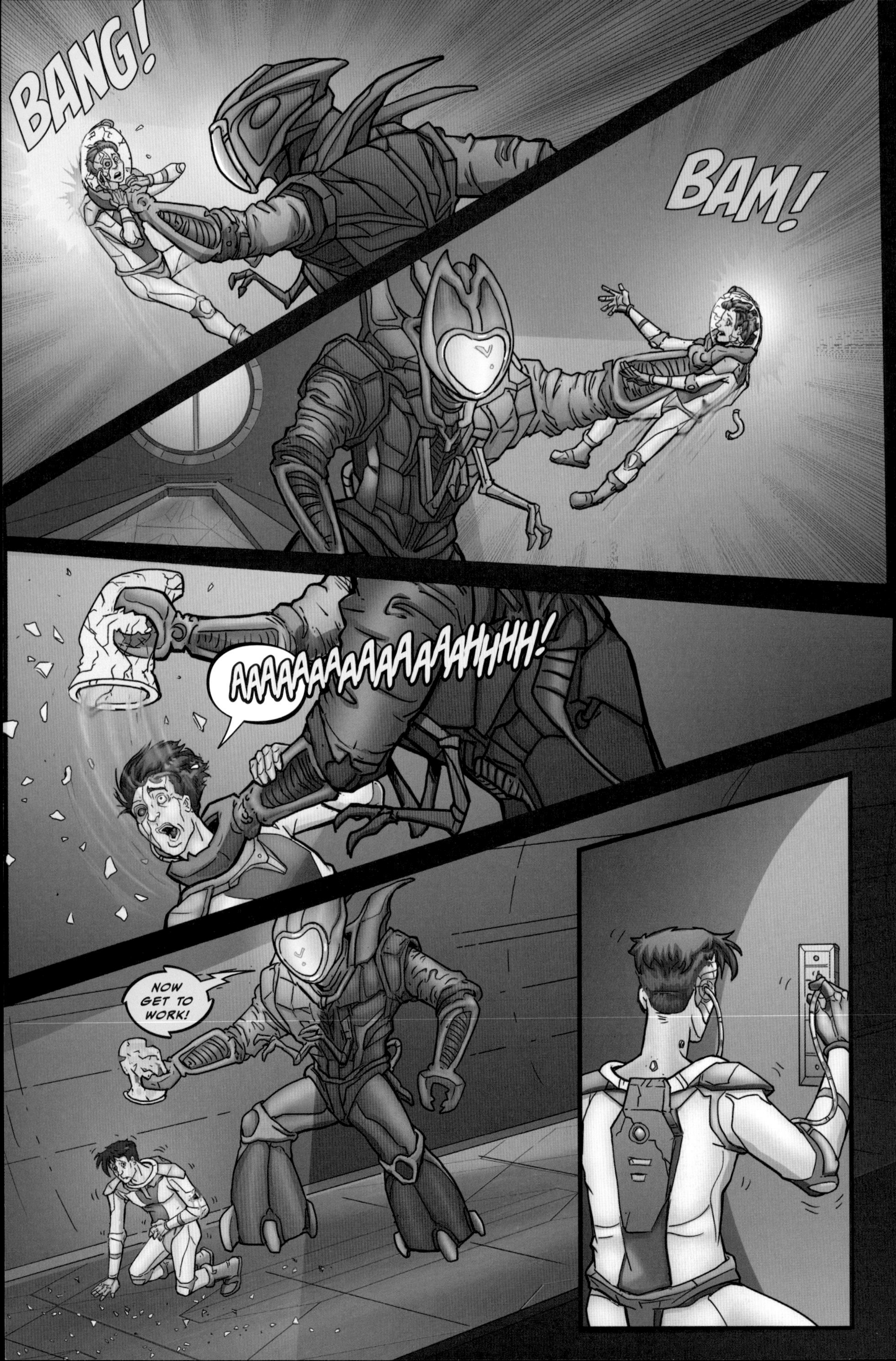
BANG!
BAM!
AAAAAAAAAAAAAAHHHH!
NOW GET TO WORK!

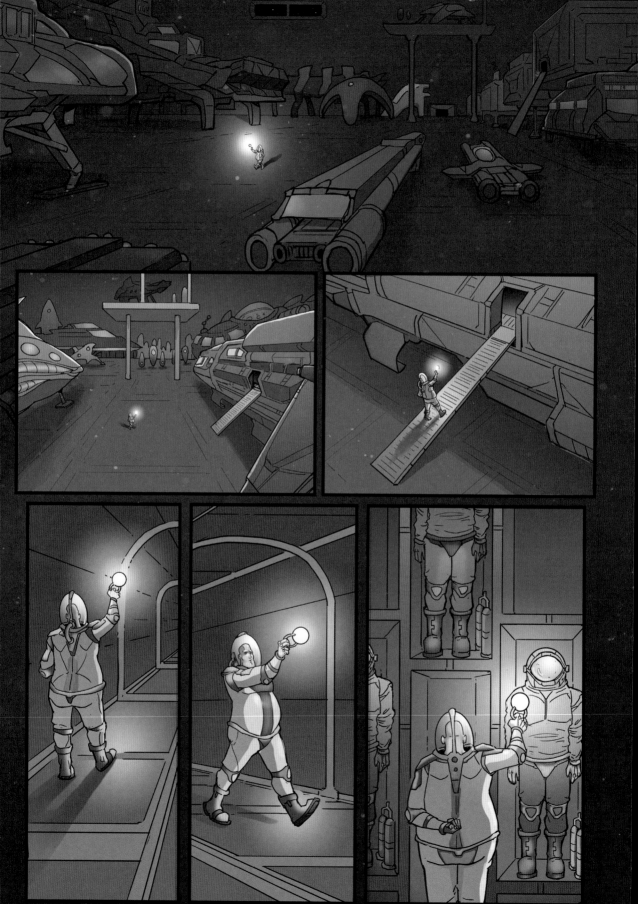

MAOW?

PUUUURRRRRRRR

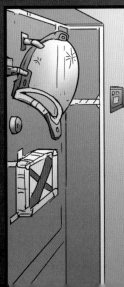

SHOO, SHOO.

MAOW.

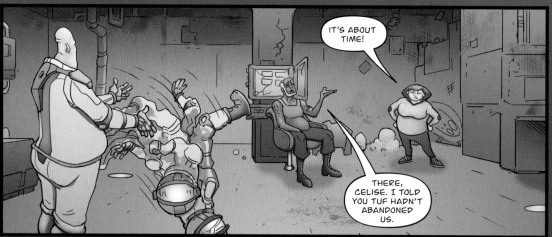

IT'S ABOUT TIME!

THERE, CELISE. I TOLD YOU TUF HADN'T ABANDONED US.

MUSHROOM IS OUTSIDE.

WELL, YES. COULDN'T YOU HAVE GOTTEN A SMALLER SIZE, AND ARE YOU SURE THESE SUITS STILL EVEN WORK?

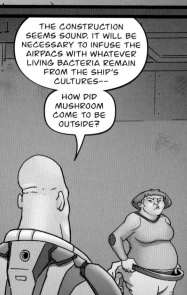

THE CONSTRUCTION SEEMS SOUND. IT WILL BE NECESSARY TO INFUSE THE AIRPACS WITH WHATEVER LIVING BACTERIA REMAIN FROM THE SHIP'S CULTURES--

HOW DID MUSHROOM COME TO BE OUTSIDE?

UH, YES. YOU SEE CELISE WAS AFRAID YOU WEREN'T COMING BACK, TUF.

A BASE AND UNFOUNDED SUSPICION.

RIGHT, WELL, UH . . .

IT'S YOUR OWN FAULT! I THOUGHT YOU WEREN'T COMING BACK, AND YOU MADE ME NERVOUS, YOU KNOW, WITH ALL YOUR PLAGUE TALK.

I TRIED TO CATCH THE LITTLE ONE, BUT IT KEPT RUNNING AND HISSING AT ME. ANYWAY, THE BIG GRAY ONE LET ME PICK IT RIGHT UP.

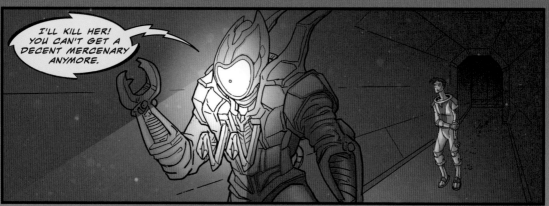

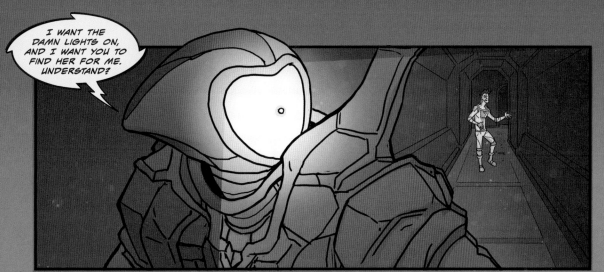

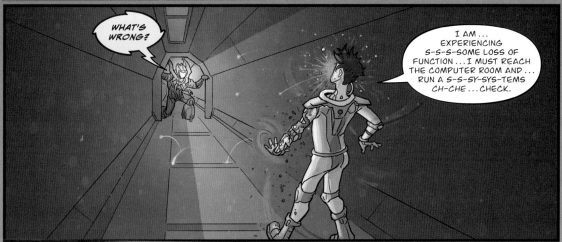

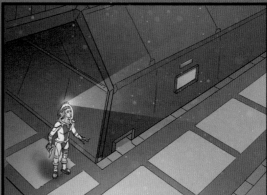

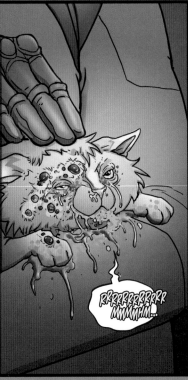

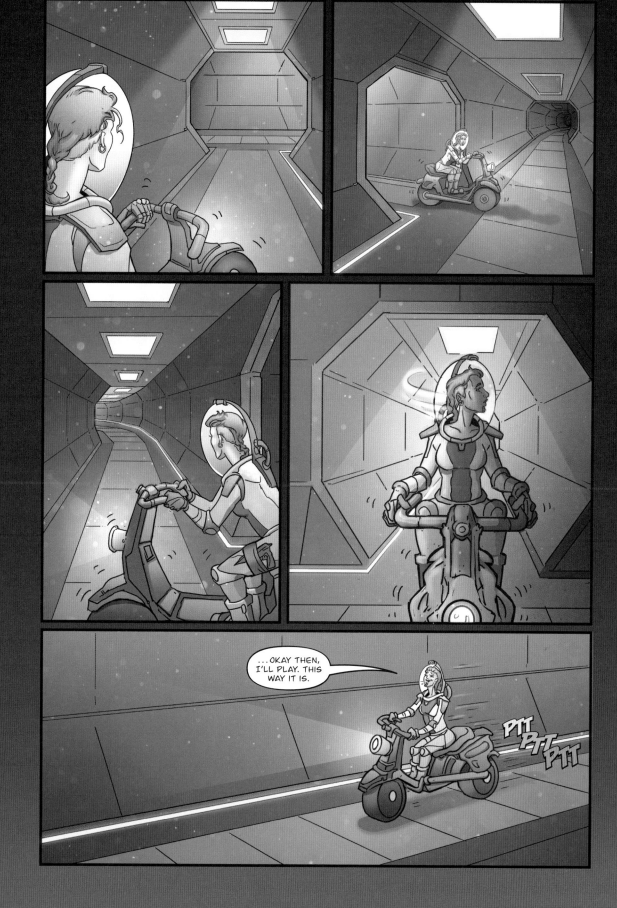

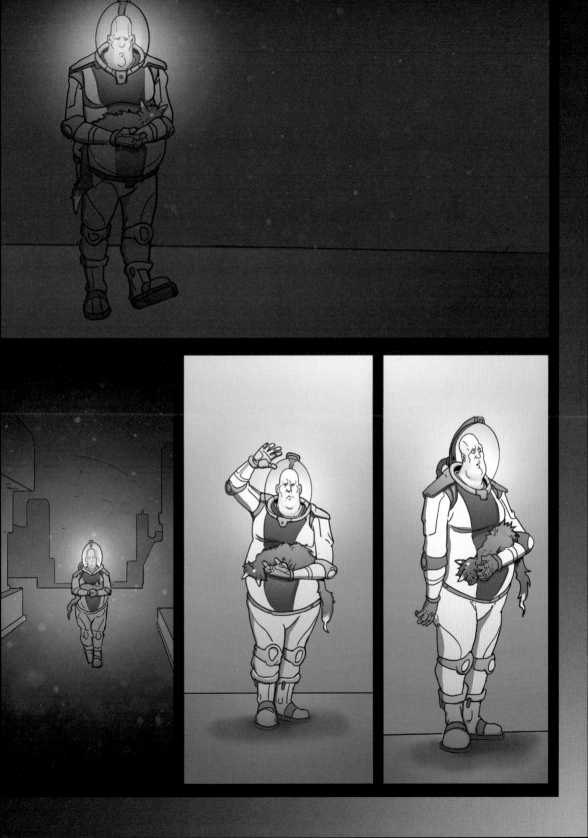

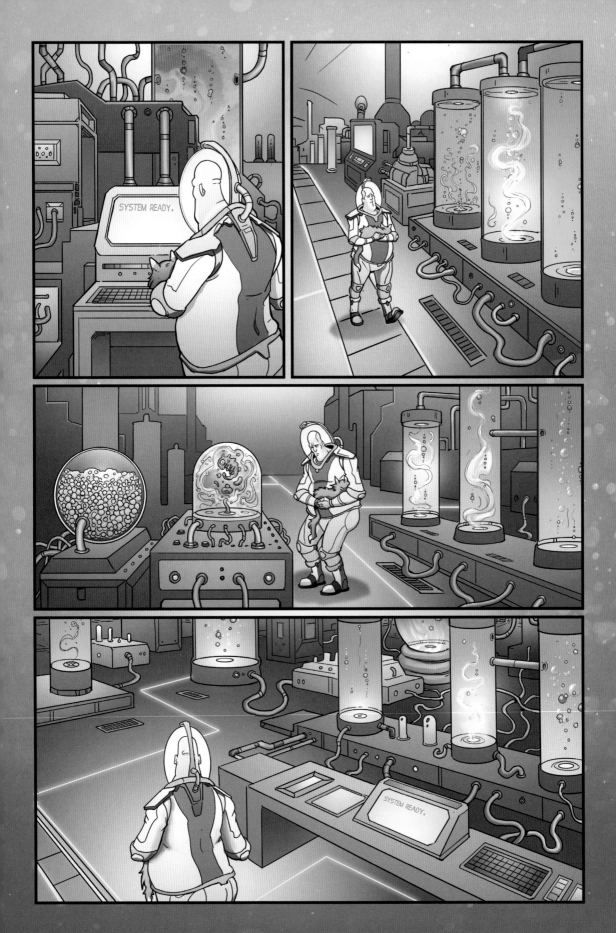

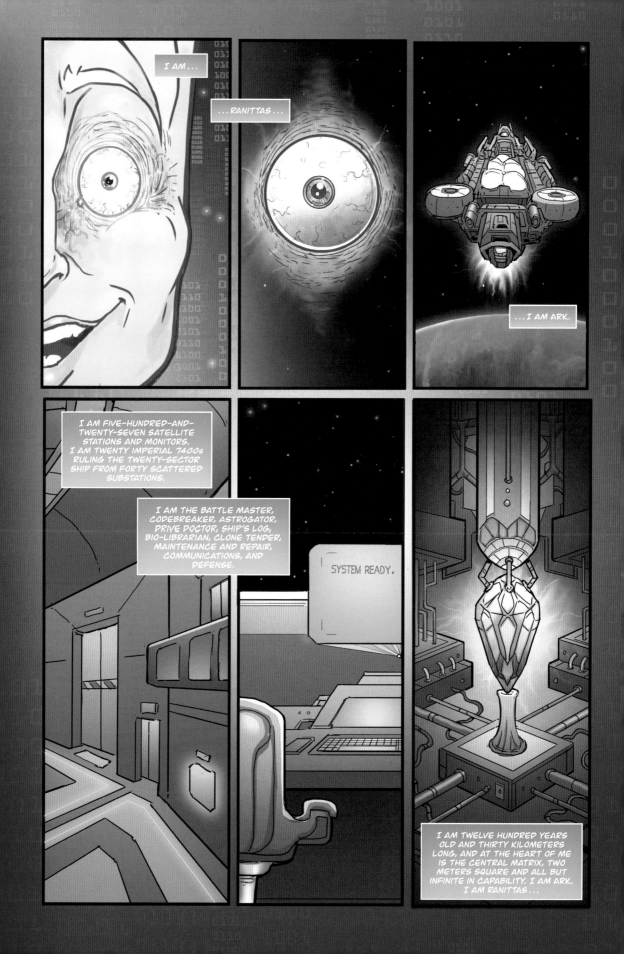

...AND I AM DYING.

WAKE UP, YOU USELESS PILE OF JUNK.

...YOU FOOL.

WATCH YOUR MOUTH.

FOOL. I SAID FOOL, AND FOOL IT IS.

HEH HEH HEH.

YOU KILLED ME, KAJ, AND FOR NOTHING...FOR IMPATIENCE. I COULD HAVE GIVEN IT ALL TO YOU. THE SHIP IS EMPTY, THEY'RE ALL DEAD. AND THE SYSTEM IS EMPTY TOO.

I WAS ALL ALONE IN THERE. NO OTHER MIND IN THE CIRCUITS, KAJ. THE ARK IS AN IDIOT GIANT.

THOSE EARTH IMPERIALS KNEW THE SEEDSHIPS WERE TOO POWERFUL TO LEAVE IN THE HANDS OF ANY A.I.-- THEY KNEW THAT AS THEY BUILT THEM.

"SO, IT NEEDED THEM, THE CREW. EVEN JUST ONE PERSON COULD WORK THE SYSTEM. A SYSTEM DESIGNED TO REPAIR ITSELF AND DEFEND ITSELF AND DO A THOUSAND OTHER THINGS...

"...IF YOU TELL IT TO. IT REALLY ONLY NEEDS ONE PERSON. CAN YOU IMAGINE? ONE PERSON! AND YOU COULD HAVE BEEN THAT MAN, KAJ NEVIS.

"BUT NO, YOU GOT IMPATIENT AND KILLED ME."

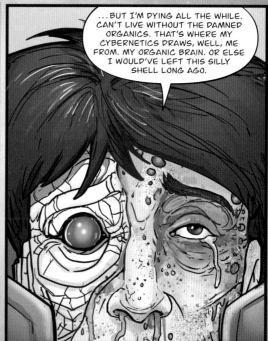

"THE SHIP WAS HORRIBLY UNDERMANNED IN ITS LAST DAYS-- ONLY THIRTY-TWO LEFT--AND THERE WAS AN ATTACK, A HRUUN ATTACK. THEY BROKE THE CODE, OPENED THE DOME, AND LANDED.

"THE HRUUN STORMED UP THE HALLS, MORE THAN A HUNDRED OF THEM. THEY WERE WINNING, THREATENING TO TAKE THE SHIP. THE DEFENDERS FOUGHT THEM EVERY STEP OF THE WAY, SEALED OFF WHOLE SECTORS OF THE ARK, EVACUATED ALL THE AIR, TURNED OFF ALL THE POWER.

"THERE ARE STILL PLACES THAT ARE BATTLE-SCARRED, DYSFUNCTIONAL, BEYOND THE ARK'S REPAIR CAPABILITIES.

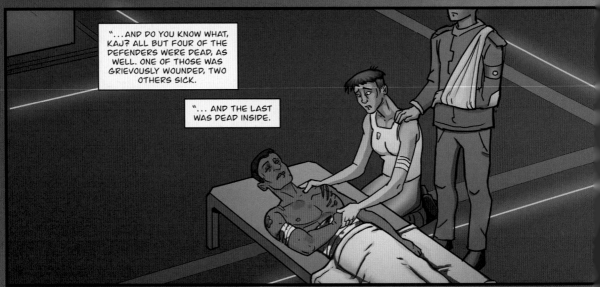

"...AND DO YOU KNOW WHAT, KAJ? ALL BUT FOUR OF THE DEFENDERS WERE DEAD, AS WELL. ONE OF THOSE WAS GRIEVOUSLY WOUNDED, TWO OTHERS SICK.

"...AND THE LAST WAS DEAD INSIDE.

"THEY GOT A FEW THAT WAY. THEY SET UP AMBUSHES, FOUGHT THEM METER BY METER.

"THE DEFENDERS LET LOOSE THEIR PLAGUES AND PESTILENCE AND PARASITES, AND FROM THE SHIP'S VATS THEY SUMMONED PET NIGHTMARES, AND THEY FOUGHT, AND DIED, AND WON.

"IN THE END, ALL THE HRUUN WERE DEAD . . .

". . .WOULD YOU LIKE TO KNOW THEIR NAMES? NO, I THOUGHT NOT. YOU HAVE NO CURIOSITY.

"IT IS NO MATTER. TUF WILL WANT TO KNOW, AS WILL LEON, NO DOUBT--"

TUF? LEON? WHAT ARE YOU TALKING ABOUT? THEY'LL BE DEAD, BOTH OF THEM.

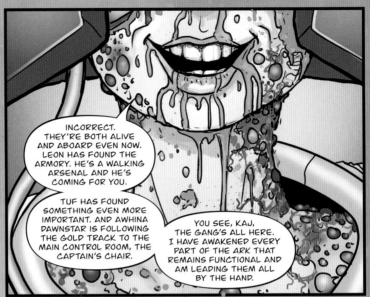

INCORRECT. THEY'RE BOTH ALIVE AND ABOARD EVEN NOW. LEON HAS FOUND THE ARMORY. HE'S A WALKING ARSENAL AND HE'S COMING FOR YOU.

TUF HAS FOUND SOMETHING EVEN MORE IMPORTANT. AND AWHINA DAWNSTAR IS FOLLOWING THE GOLD TRACK TO THE MAIN CONTROL ROOM, THE CAPTAIN'S CHAIR.

YOU SEE, KAJ, THE GANG'S ALL HERE. I HAVE AWAKENED EVERY PART OF THE ARK THAT REMAINS FUNCTIONAL AND AM LEADING THEM ALL BY THE HAND.

THEN STOP IT!

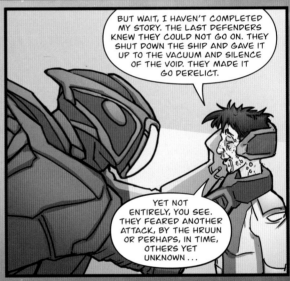

BUT WAIT, I HAVEN'T COMPLETED MY STORY. THE LAST DEFENDERS KNEW THEY COULD NOT GO ON. THEY SHUT DOWN THE SHIP AND GAVE IT UP TO THE VACUUM AND SILENCE OF THE VOID. THEY MADE IT GO DERELICT.

YET NOT ENTIRELY, YOU SEE. THEY FEARED ANOTHER ATTACK, BY THE HRUUN OR PERHAPS, IN TIME, OTHERS YET UNKNOWN . . .

" . . . SO, THEY TOLD THE ARK TO DEFEND ITSELF. THEY ARMED THE PLASMA CANNON AND EXTERNAL LASERS AND KEPT THE DEFENSE SPHERE FUNCTIONAL, AS WE LEARNED TO OUR SORROW . . .

" . . . AND THEY PROGRAMMED THE SHIP TO TAKE A TERRIBLE VENGEANCE FOR THEM, TO RETURN AGAIN AND AGAIN AND AGAIN TO HRO B'RANA, FROM WHENCE THE HRUUN HAD COME, AND TO DELIVER ITS GIFTS OF PLAGUES AND PESTILENCE AND DEATH.

"TO GUARD AGAINST THE HRUUN FROM EVER BUILDING UP IMMUNITY, THEY PROGRAMMED THEIR PLAGUE TANKS FOR ENDLESS MUTATIONS, TO FASHION EVER NEWER AND MORE DEADLY VIRUSES.

I DON'T GIVE A DAMN ABOUT ANY OF THAT NOISE. HAVE YOU STOPPED THE OTHERS? CAN YOU KILL THEM NOW? I WARN YOU, DO IT OR YOU'RE DEAD.

I'M DEAD ANYWAY, I'VE TOLD YOU THAT. THEY LEFT A SECONDARY DEFENSE IN PLACE SHOULD THE SHIP BE BREACHED AGAIN.

THE ARK IS PROGRAMMED TO WAKE ITSELF AND FILL THE CORRIDORS WITH ATMOSPHERE TAINTED BY A DOZEN DIFFERENT DISEASE VECTORS.

THE ONE I'VE CONTRACTED HAS NO NAME, SOME KIND OF SPORE, I THINK.

THERE ARE ANTIGENS AND VACCINES, AUTOMATICALLY BEING MANUFACTURED FOR THE CREW. BUT IT'S TOO LATE FOR ME, AND IT'S TOO LATE FOR YOU, KAJ. TOGETHER WE COULD HAVE HAD ENOUGH POWER TO RIVAL THE GODS. INSTEAD, WE DIE.

HOW ABOUT YOU DIE, AND THE SHIP IS MINE!

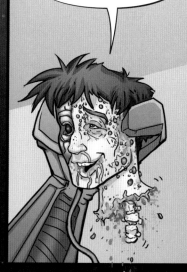

I THINK NOT... I HAVE KICKED THE BRAINLESS GIANT SOUNDLY, AND IT IS AWAKE. STILL BRAINLESS, OH YES, BUT AWAKE, AND READY FOR ORDERS YOU HAVE NEITHER THE KNOWLEDGE NOR THE CAPACITY TO GIVE.

I AM LEADING JEFRI LEON STRAIGHT HERE, AND AWHINA DAWNSTAR IS ASCENDING TOWARD CENTRAL CONTROL EVEN NOW ... AND MORE ...

I AM WAKING UP THE REAL NIGHTMARES, KAJ. THEY'RE AWAKENING, AND THEY WANT TO MEET YOU ... DO YOU WANT TO HEAR MORE?

NO MORE!

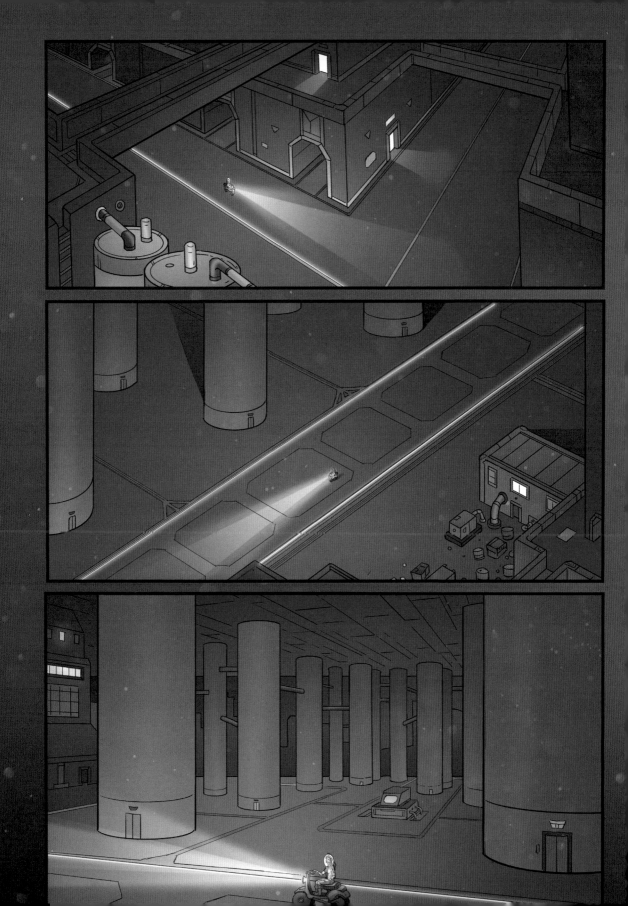

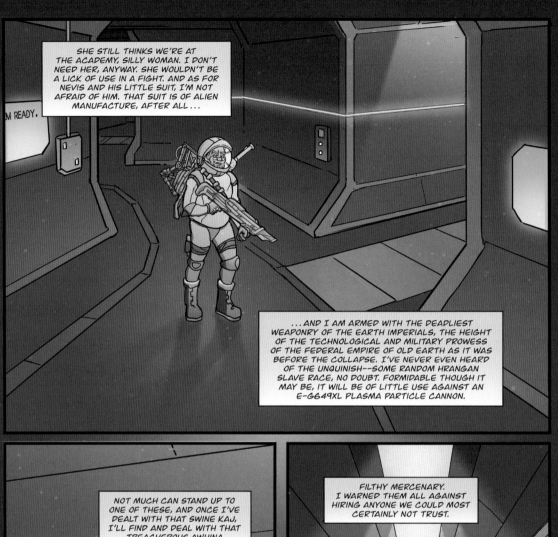

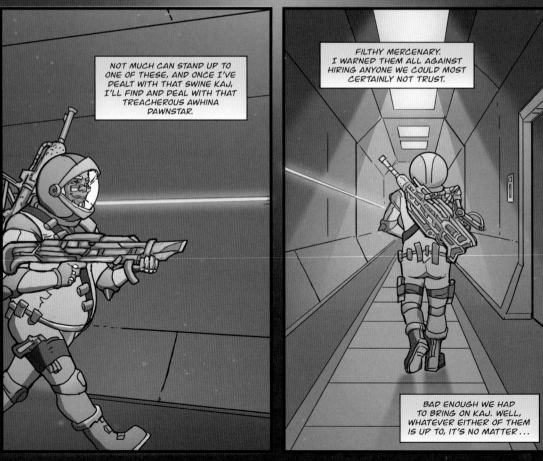

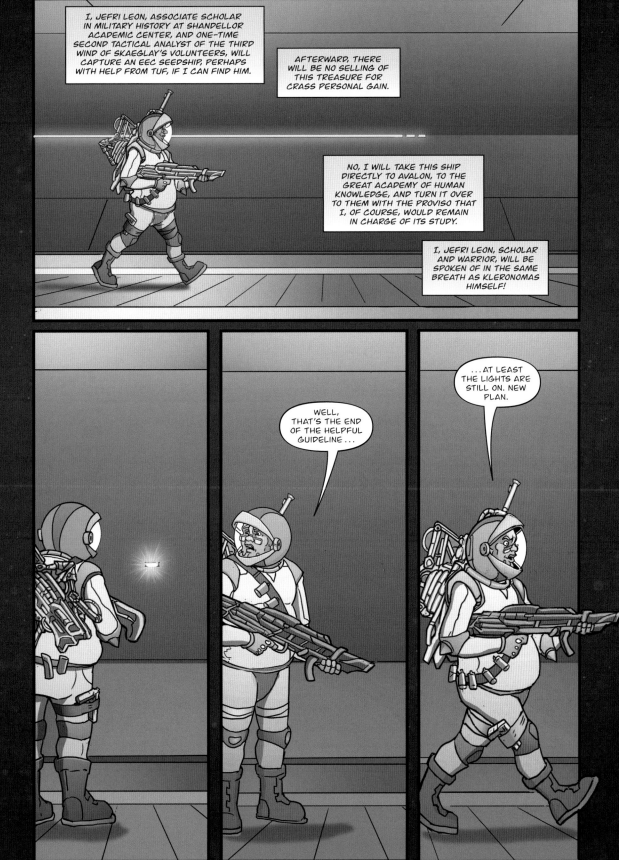

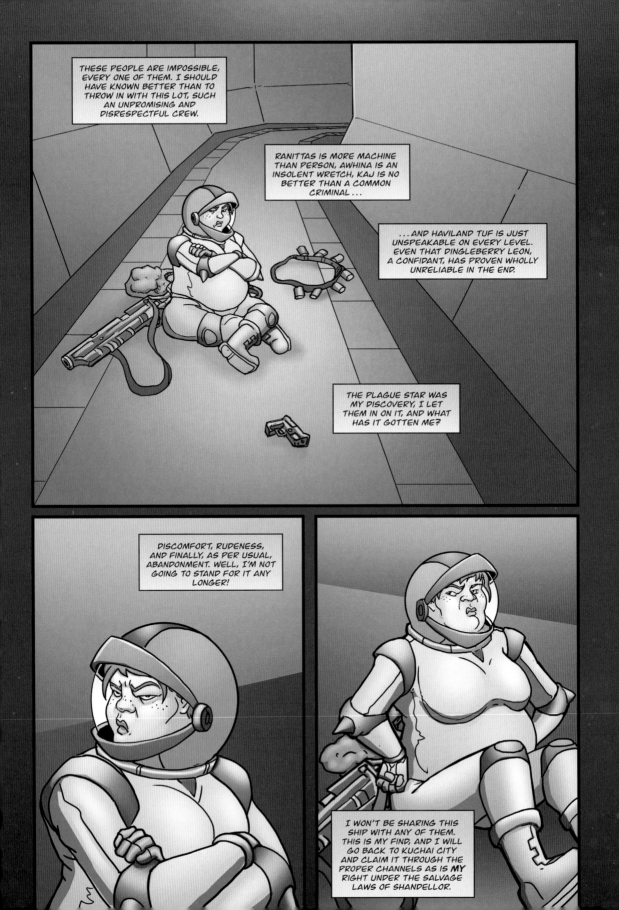

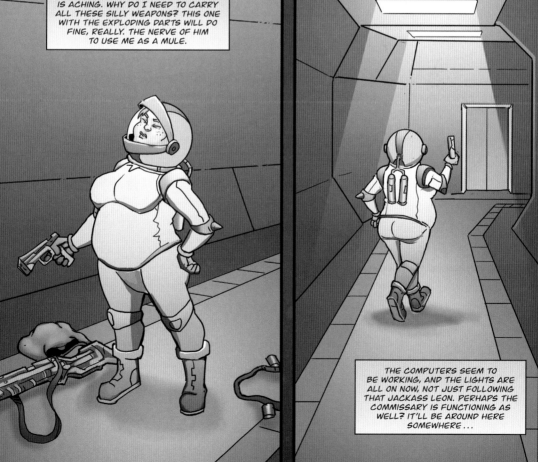

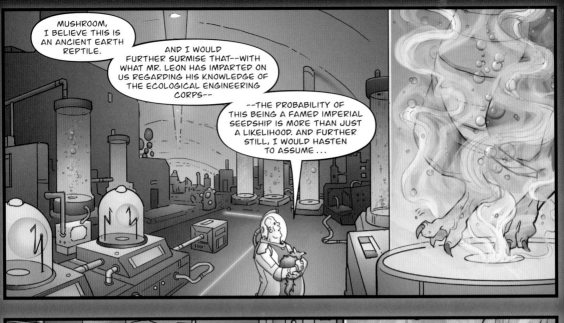

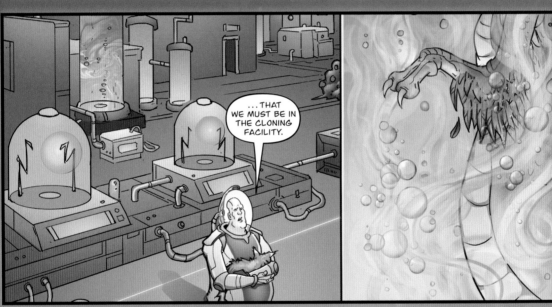

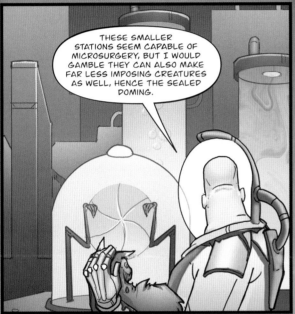

SCREW THEM, SCREW THEM ALL. THAT PIECE OF CRAP RANITTAS SHOULD HAVE BEEN MORE USEFUL.

SO WHAT IF THE AIR IS CONTAMINATED?! IT WAS THEIR OWN FUCKING FAULT FOR NOT LISTENING.

ATTN : OXYGEN LEVEL : LOW

AND WHAT THE HELL IS THIS? IT LOOKS LIKE I'M GOING TO HAVE TO BE QUICKER THAN I HOPED TO BE...

OXYGEN'S ALMOST OUT, AND I CAN'T LEAVE THE SUIT TILL EVERYONE ELSE IS DEAD AND I CAN CLEAN UP THE DAMNED AIR.

THAT FREAK RANITTAS SAID SOMETHING ABOUT DAWNSTAR ALREADY BEING ON THE CONTROL DECK...

WELL, THIS IS A NICE CHANGE OF PACE.

I LIKE THIS CHAIR, BUT THIS STATION IS JUST A READOUT POINT--NOT ABLE TO GET A LOT DONE HERE. WOULD BE A HELL OF A LOT EASIER IF I HAD SIX BUDDIES HELPING ME OUT, BUT IT'LL HAVE TO DO, YEAH? AND I'M SECURE--THAT BAR IN THE ELEVATOR DOOR IS GOING TO STOP ANYONE FROM SNEAKING UP ON ME.

EVERY STATION MUST HAVE ITS OWN SUBSTATION ELSEWHERE, BUT I CAN ALWAYS COUNTER ANY COMMAND FROM UP HERE.

THIS HERE IS MY ACE CARD . . . THIS IS THE WHOLE CAKE AND POTATOES. SO, WHAT DO WE GOT?

FULL DIAGNOSTIC REPORT ON THE WAY, SUBSECTIONS ALL ACTIVATED, THOSE THAT CAN BE, ANYWAY . . . SOMETHING BATSHIT CRAZY HAPPENED IN HERE AT SOME POINT, FOR SURE.

THE BIODEFENSE IS REALLY CRANKING . . . **SHIT**, THESE ARE DISEASES. I HAVEN'T EVEN HEARD OF HALF OF THESE. IMPRESSIVE.

RANITTAS HAS OBVIOUSLY GONE TO THE GREAT PROGRAM BEYOND THE UNIVERSE BY NOW. I'M SURE IT WASN'T PRETTY.

MY SUIT HAS PLENTY OF RECYCLING BACTERIA IN THE TANKS TO LAST AWHILE, BUT I SHOULD STILL CLEAN OUT A FEW SECTIONS OF THIS SHIP, OR IT'S GOING TO GET PRETTY GAMEY PRETTY QUICK INSIDE SAID SUIT.

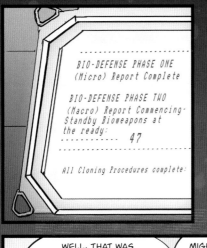

BIO-DEFENSE PHASE ONE
(Micro) Report Complete

BIO-DEFENSE PHASE TWO
(Macro) Report Commencing-
Standby Bioweapons at
the ready:
.... 47

All Cloning Procedures complete:

WHAT'S IT DOING NOW? MACRO, WHAT'S THAT MEAN, BIG PLAGUES?

Malfunctions in vats:

671 - 3471 - 4489:
Malfunctions aborted;
stasis fields terminat
Release Cycle Commencin

Species #22-774-88639-0409
Homeworld: Vilkakis
Common name: Hooded Dracula

Initiating Release Cycle
3 --- 2 --- 1 ---
RELEASED

WELL, THAT WAS FAST. I'VE HEARD OF THESE BAD BOYS, THEY'RE NASTY THINGS. SOME KIND OF FLYING NOCTURNAL BLOODSUCKER WITH A REAL SHITTY ATTITUDE, INSANELY AGGRESSIVE BUT PRETTY DIM.

MIGHT BE A PROBLEM FOR MY BUDDY KAJ, BUT PROBABLY NOT IN THAT SUIT OF HIS. AND MY SUIT IS PRETTY FLIMSY, SO IS THIS A KAJ NEVIS PROBLEM OR A ME PROBLEM?

AND WHAT'S THIS NEW ONE?

Species #13-412-71425--8812
Homeworld: Abatiora
Common name: Hellkitten

Initiating Release Cycle
3 --- 2 --- 1 ---
RELEASED

Species #33-102-95469-1269
Homeworld: Jayden Two
Common name: Walking Web

HELLKITTENS? HAVEN'T HEARD OF THOSE, BUT I KNOW ANYTHING THAT COMES FROM THAT SHITHOLE ABATIORA HAS TO BE NASTY ENOUGH--NOT MUCH CAN SURVIVE THERE.

Initiating Release Cycle
3 --- 2 --- 1 ---
RELEASED

Species #54-754-37377-84921
Homeworld: PSC92,
TSC746, likely other
UNNAMED asteroids.

Common name: Rolleram

AND ANOTHER, OH TERRIFIC. HOW MANY HUNGRY BEASTIES DOES THIS SHIP HAVE?

FORTY-SEVEN BIOWEAPONS WAS IT? NO, NO THIS WON'T DO, NOT AT ALL.

DIAGNOSTICS

CENTRAL MATR

Release Cycle
D 1

A3 A37-37307-921
or Craxis

o name D'undles

ting Release Cycle

EATE

LOWER LEVEL DAMAGE REPORT

Levels 4B - 4K 57% Damage
Air pressure malfunction
Level 4F zero circulation
Response level-magenta

Levels 11Y - 120 varifing
Level 18U Recalibrating

ONLY FIVE GOT LOOSE, SO THAT'S NOT TOO BAD, I GUESS. THERE'S NO ONE ELSE OUT THERE BUT THAT JACKASS NEVIS. SO, THERE'S THAT.

WHAT'S THIS LAST ONE THAT GOT BY ME?

LIST OF RELEASED BIOWEAPONS: HELLKITTENS, HOODED ZRAVOLA, WALKING HEX, ROLLER BOB, TYRANNOSAURUS

LIST OF ABORTED BIOWEAPONS: D'UNDLES, UHICHETS, RAHROT

THE HELL IS A TYRANNOSAURUS, ANYWAY?

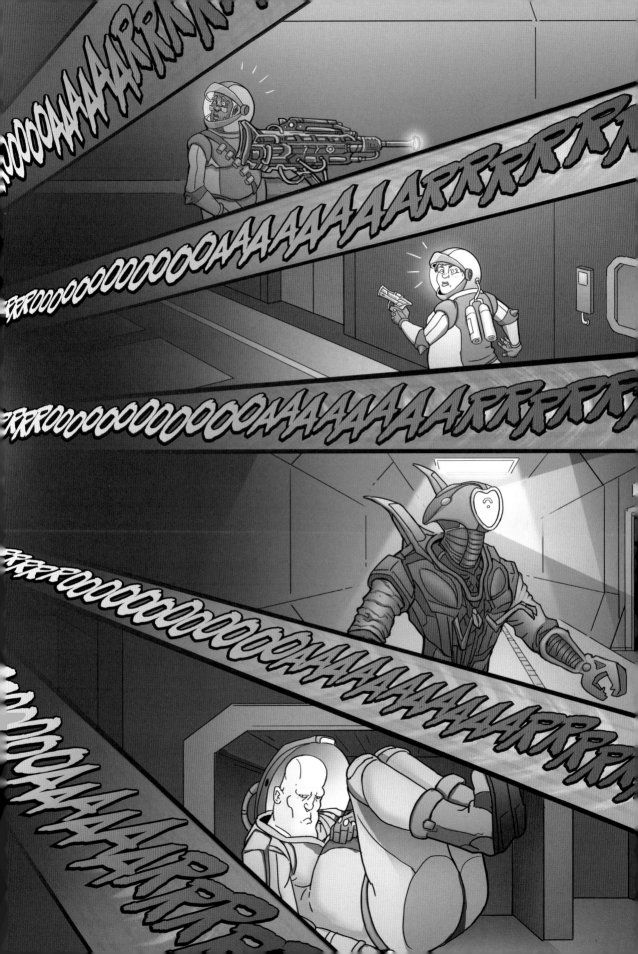

WELL YOU DON'T LOOK THAT BAD. YOU'RE QUIET, ANYWAY. HERE, KITTY, KITTY . . .
HIIIIIIISSSSSSSSSSSSSS...
ACK!
...SSSSSSSSSSSSSSSSSS!
BLAM
SPLAT

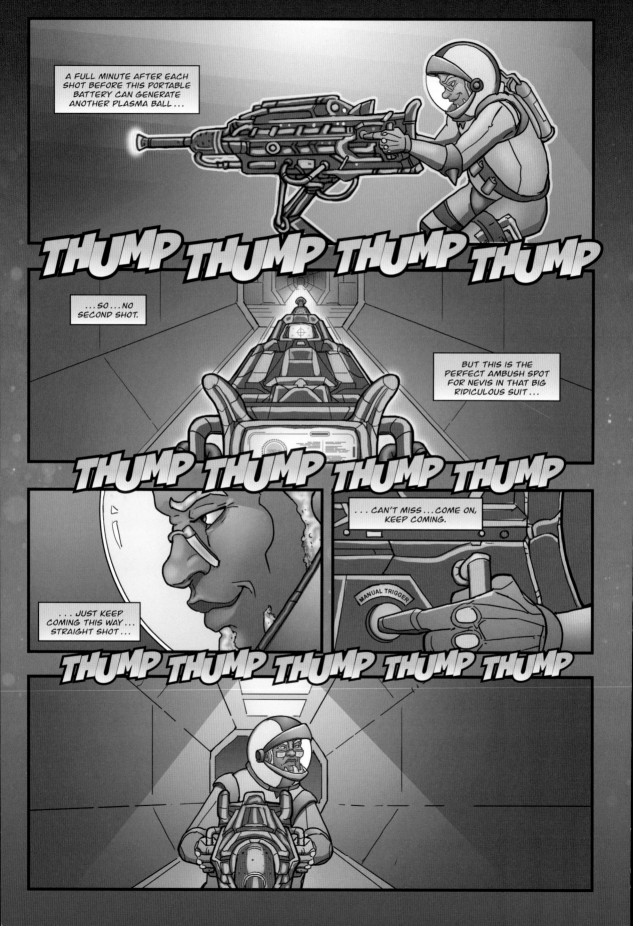

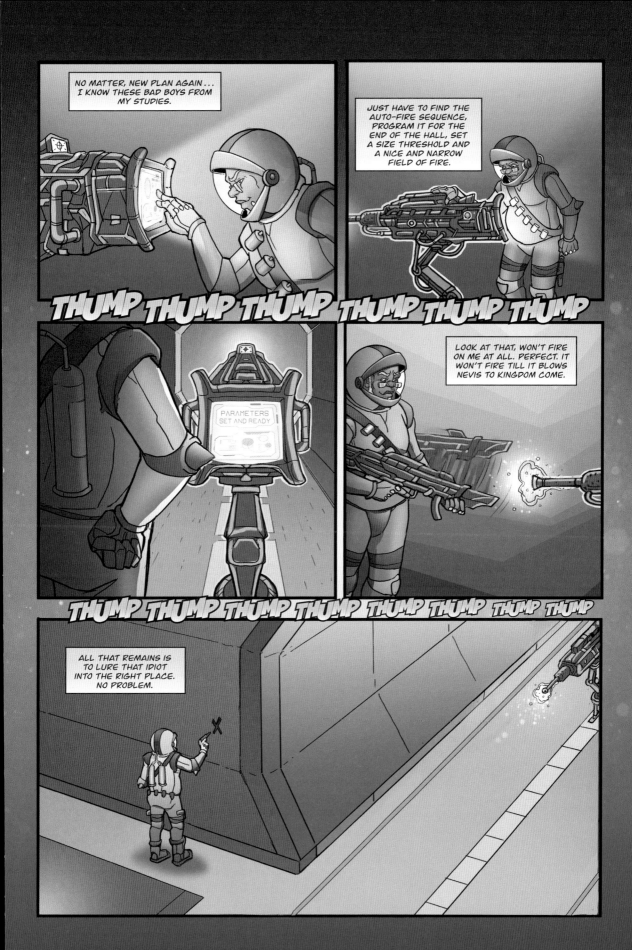

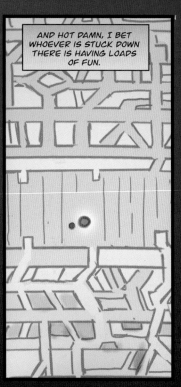

THUMP THUMP THUMP THUMP THUMP

BLAM

WE MEET AGAIN, SWINE!

SO WE DO, LEON. IT'S GOOD TO SEE YOU.

ROOOOAAAARRR

RODELYIAN POP-BERRIES ARE PROBABLY THE SWEETEST...

...ESPECIALLY WHEN FRESH, ALTHOUGH I WOULD NOT BALK AT FREEZE-DRIED, PERHAPS IN HONEY, OR AN UNPASTEURIZED MILK. I WONDER IF THERE ARE BOVINES AVAILABLE ON THIS SHIP?

I AM CURIOUS TO KNOW IF KYROSHLING OR TIBERETIAN ALE IS STRONGER? AND WOULD THE SETTLERS ON KHAI-CHUG ALPHA 535 DISAGREE TO EITHER?

...I DETECT A REDUCTION IN NOISE. PERHAPS MY NEW ACQUAINTANCE HAS CHOSEN TO VACATE THE PREMISES AFTER THE FUTILITY OF THEIR ATTEMPTS TO ROUST ME.

THEY OBVIOUSLY WOULD WIN THE BATTLE WERE I TO CONSIDER THEIR RADIOACTIVE YEASTS, BUT I FEEL THAT IS AN UNFAIR ADVANTAGE. ALTHOUGH THEIR ALE IS INDEED QUITE POTENT AND TASTY...

THUD THUD THUD THUD THUD THUD

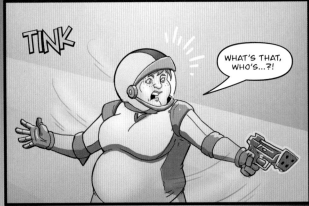

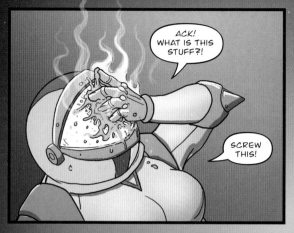

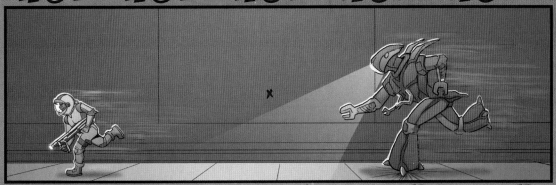

...WHY DID HE STOP?

COME ON NOW, NEVIS. IS THIS OLD SOLIDER TOO FAST FOR YOU?

HEH HEH HEH ...

WHAT'S SO FUNNY?

HEH HEH ... HAVE A LOOK ABOVE YOU AND YOU'LL SEE.

HOW DUMB DO YOU THINK I AM?

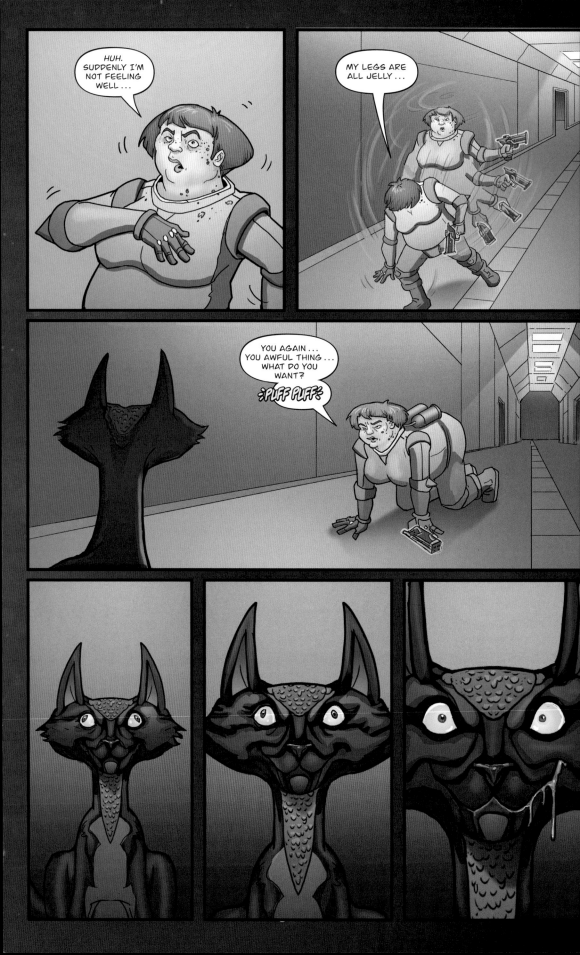

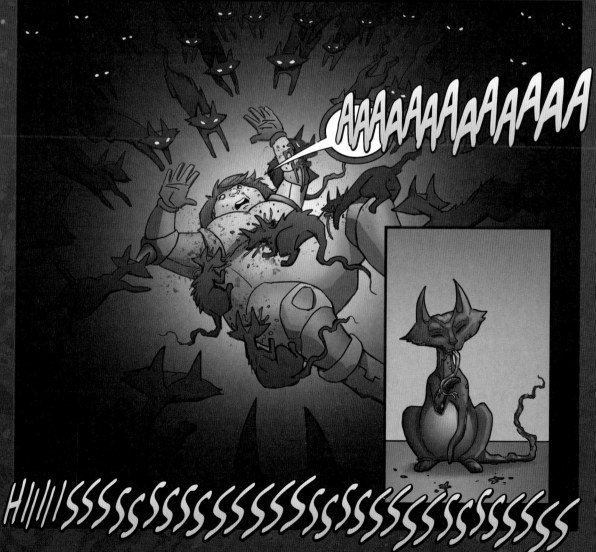

SO, IT'S DOWN TO JUST NEVIS, ME, AND TUF... TUF'S NO PROBLEM. NO, THE REAL PROBLEM HERE CONTINUES TO BE NEVIS AND HIS DAMNED UNQUIN BATTLESUIT. HE'S ALREADY DISPATCHED THE HOODED DRACULA...

...SO, LET SEE, I HAVE THREE BEASTIES STILL A' ROAMING THESE HALLS.

MAYBE ANOTHER LITTLE ZOOLOGY LESSON IS IN ORDER?

I THINK ALL THAT'S NEEDED HERE IS TO MAKE THE PROPER INTRODUCTIONS. I WONDER JUST HOW DEVIOUS A MIND THAT MUPPET REALLY HAS...

SECURITY

HEH HEH HEH. NOT DEVIOUS ENOUGH.

PART FIVE: THE DUEL

THE NEUTRINO BATH IS THINNING...

...IT SEEMS TO BE MOMENTS FROM COMPLETION. AND UPON FURTHER CONTEMPLATION...

...I HAVE COME TO REALIZE THAT IT WILL DO NO GOOD FOR MY NEW FRIEND TO COME OUT INTO THIS CRUEL WORLD AND FACE THE SAME UNTIMELY END AS THEIR PREDECESSOR.

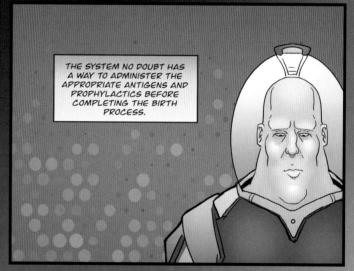

THE SYSTEM NO DOUBT HAS A WAY TO ADMINISTER THE APPROPRIATE ANTIGENS AND PROPHYLACTICS BEFORE COMPLETING THE BIRTH PROCESS.

YOU MAY COME OUT NOW, LITTLE FRIEND. I MEAN YOU NO HARM.

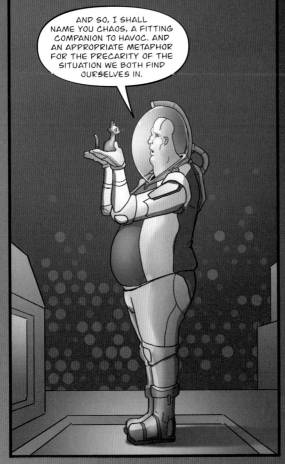

WELL, LITTLE ONE, I AM PLEASED TO HAVE SURVEYED THE IMMEDIATE AREA THOROUGHLY.

AND THE ACQUISITION OF THIS VEHICLE HAS BEEN OVERWHELMINGLY HELPFUL. IT IS NICE TO BE SITTING, AS MY BACK WAS BOTHERING ME SOMEWHAT.

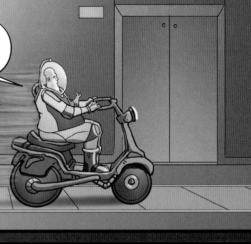

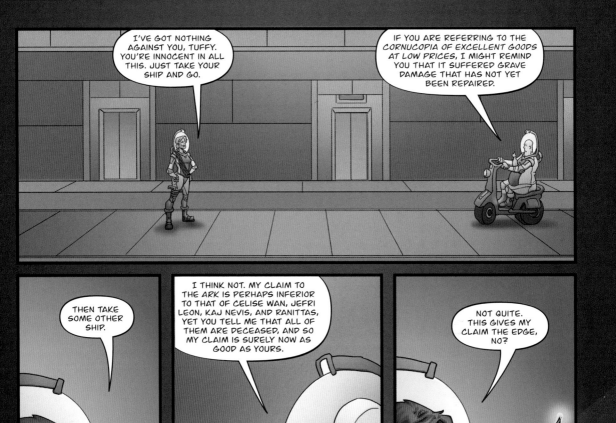

I'VE GOT NOTHING AGAINST YOU, TUFFY. YOU'RE INNOCENT IN ALL THIS. JUST TAKE YOUR SHIP AND GO.

IF YOU ARE REFERRING TO THE CORNUCOPIA OF EXCELLENT GOODS AT LOW PRICES, I MIGHT REMIND YOU THAT IT SUFFERED GRAVE DAMAGE THAT HAS NOT YET BEEN REPAIRED.

THEN TAKE SOME OTHER SHIP.

I THINK NOT. MY CLAIM TO THE ARK IS PERHAPS INFERIOR TO THAT OF CELISE WAN, JEFRI LEON, KAJ NEVIS, AND RANITTAS, YET YOU TELL ME THAT ALL OF THEM ARE DECEASED, AND SO MY CLAIM IS SURELY NOW AS GOOD AS YOURS.

NOT QUITE. THIS GIVES MY CLAIM THE EDGE, NO?

HUMPH.

LET THIS BE YOUR FIRST LESSON IN THE HARD WAYS OF THE UNIVERSE, LITTLE ONE. WHAT MATTERS FAIRNESS, WHEN ONE PARTY HAS A GUN, AND THE OTHER DOES NOT? BRUTE VIOLENCE RULES EVERYWHERE, AND INTELLIGENCE AND GOOD INTENT ARE TRAMPLED UPON.

PURRRRRT

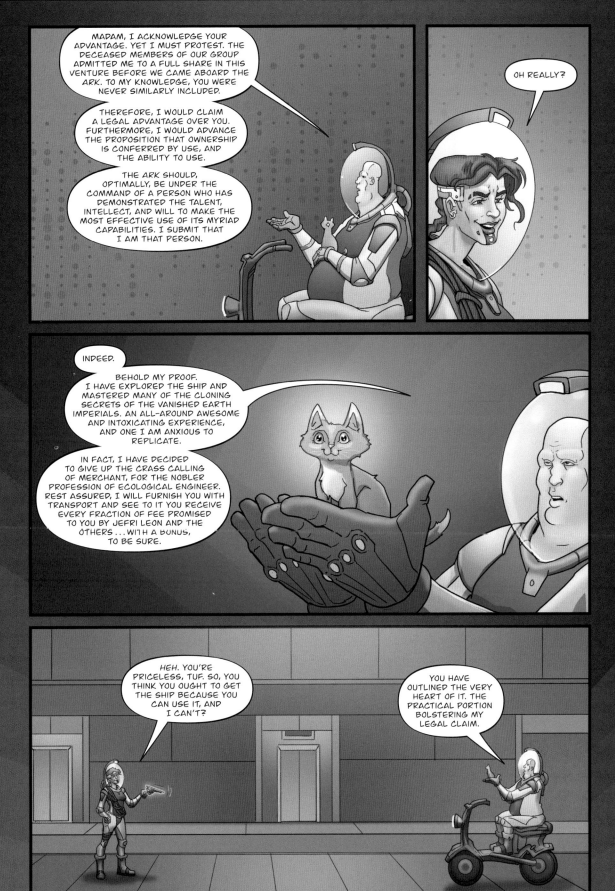

HEH HEH . . .

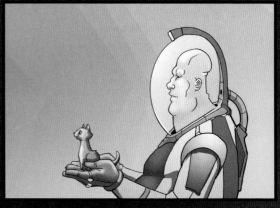

HERE, I DON'T NEED THIS . . .

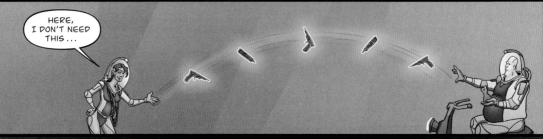

IT WOULD SEEM MY CLAIM HAS BEEN UNEXPECTEDLY AND DECISIVELY STRENGTHENED. MOMENTARILY I TOYED WITH THE CONCEPT OF US NAVIGATING THESE UNCHARTED WATERS TOGETHER, PERHAPS ENJOYING THIS GIFT OF FORTUNE AS FULL PARTNERS . . .

BUT AS I HARBOR NO DELUSIONS OF YOUR MORAL COMPASS IN THIS SITUATION, MADAM DAWNSTAR, AND I WOULD FEAR FOR MY SAFETY UNDER ANY SORT OF TRUCE WE MIGHT COME TO . . . WILL ASK YOU ONCE AGAIN TO LEAVE THE ARK. YOU ARE WELCOME TO LEAVE ROUTING DIGITS SO I CAN MAKE YOUR FULL PAYMENT IN DUE TIME . . . I WILL ASSERT THAT I MAY THREATEN TO SHOOT YOU IF YOU DO NOT COMPLY.

BUT YOU WON'T. YOU PLAY THE GAME BY THE RULES, TUF. AND I'M THE KID WHO LIKES TO KICK OVER THE BOARD. DO YOU KNOW WHAT I'VE BEEN UP TO WHILE YOU'VE BEEN CLONING YOURSELF A KITTEN?

OBVIOUSLY, I DO NOT.

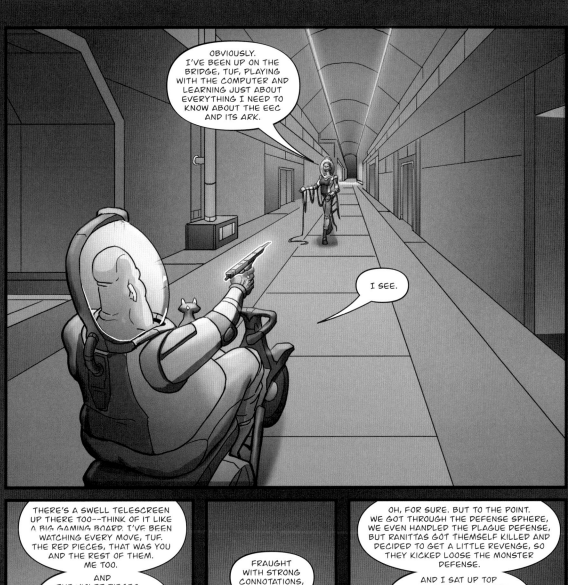

OBVIOUSLY. I'VE BEEN UP ON THE BRIDGE, TUF, PLAYING WITH THE COMPUTER AND LEARNING JUST ABOUT EVERYTHING I NEED TO KNOW ABOUT THE EEC AND ITS ARK.

I SEE.

THERE'S A SWELL TELESCREEN UP THERE TOO--THINK OF IT LIKE A BIG GAMING BOARD. I'VE BEEN WATCHING EVERY MOVE, TUF. THE RED PIECES, THAT WAS YOU AND THE REST OF THEM. ME TOO.

AND THE VIOLET PIECES-- THE BIOWEAPONS, AS THE SYSTEM CALLS THEM. I LIKE MONSTERS BETTER, MYSELF. SHORTER. LESS FORMAL.

FRAUGHT WITH STRONG CONNOTATIONS, HOWEVER.

OH, FOR SURE. BUT TO THE POINT. WE GOT THROUGH THE DEFENSE SPHERE, WE EVEN HANDLED THE PLAGUE DEFENSE, BUT RANITTAS GOT THEMSELF KILLED AND DECIDED TO GET A LITTLE REVENGE, SO THEY KICKED LOOSE THE MONSTER DEFENSE.

AND I SAT UP TOP AND WATCHED THE RED AND VIOLET DOTS CHASE EACH OTHER. BUT SOMETHING WAS MISSING, TUF. KNOW WHAT?

THUD   THUD   THUD   THUD   THUD   THUD

EXCUSE ME--

DON'T INTERRUPT. KEY QUESTION: IF THEY WERE PREPARED TO TURN LOOSE THESE CAGED HORRORS OF THEIRS TO REPEL INTRUDERS IN AN EMERGENCY . . .

. . . HOW DID THEY PREVENT THEIR OWN PEOPLE FROM GETTING KILLED?!

THUD   THUD   THUD   THUD   THUD

AN INTERESTING QUANDARY. I EAGERLY ANTICIPATE LEARNING THE ANSWER TO YOUR PUZZLE. I FEAR I WILL HAVE TO DEFER THAT PLEASURE, HOWEVER.

AHEM-- FAR BE IT FROM ME TO INTERRUPT SUCH A FASCINATING DISCOURSE. I FEEL OBLIGATED TO POINT OUT, HOWEVER--

YES?

THUD   THUD   THUD   THUD   THUD

A RATHER LARGE CARNIVOROUS BEAST HAS APPEARED BEHIND YOU AND IS ATTEMPTING TO SNEAK UP ON YOU. IT IS NOT DOING A VERY GOOD JOB.

REALLY? COME ON NOW, TUFFY! SURELY YOU DON'T EXPECT ME TO FALL FOR THE OL' THERE'S-A-MONSTER-BEHIND-YOU GAMBIT. I EXPECTED BETTER OF YOU, MATE!

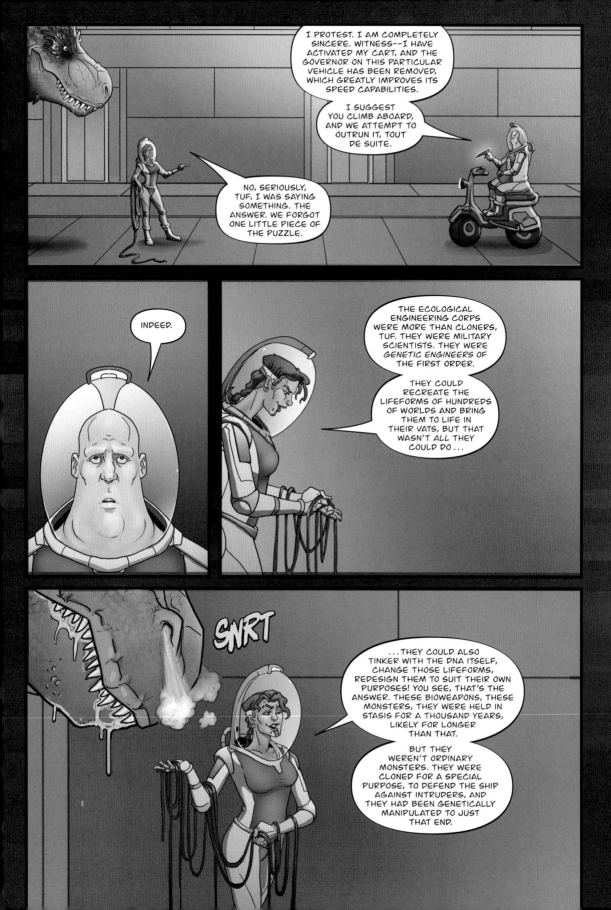

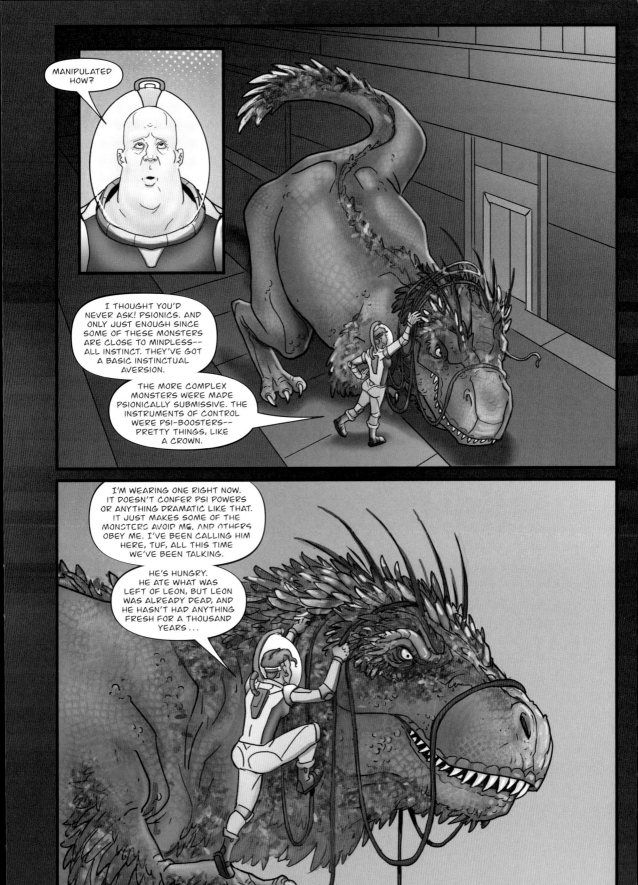

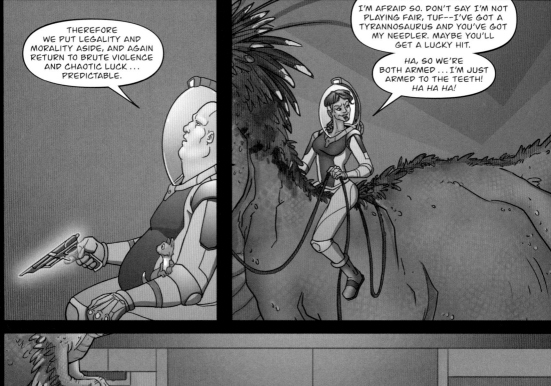

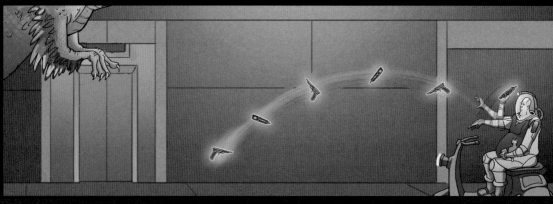

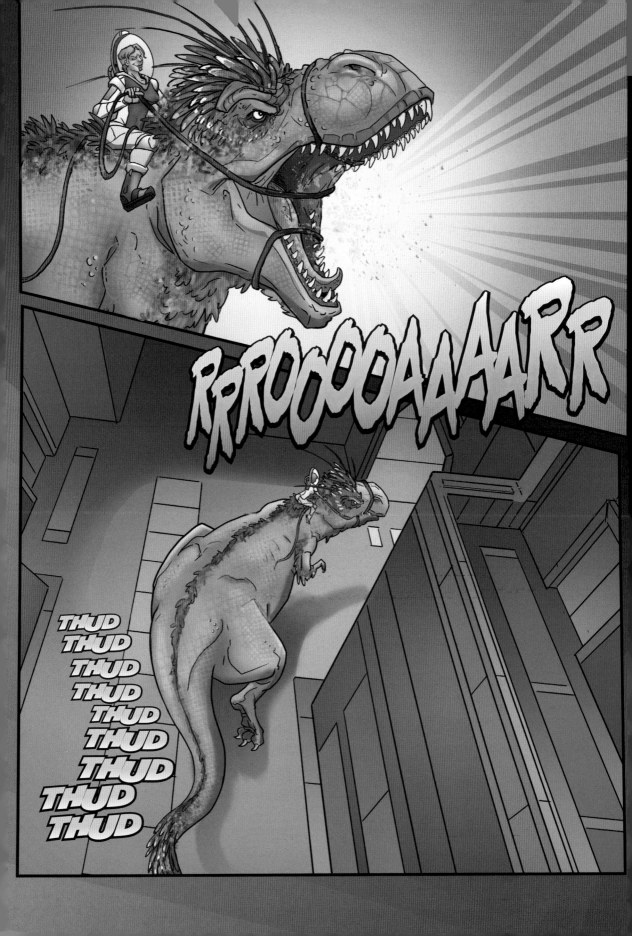

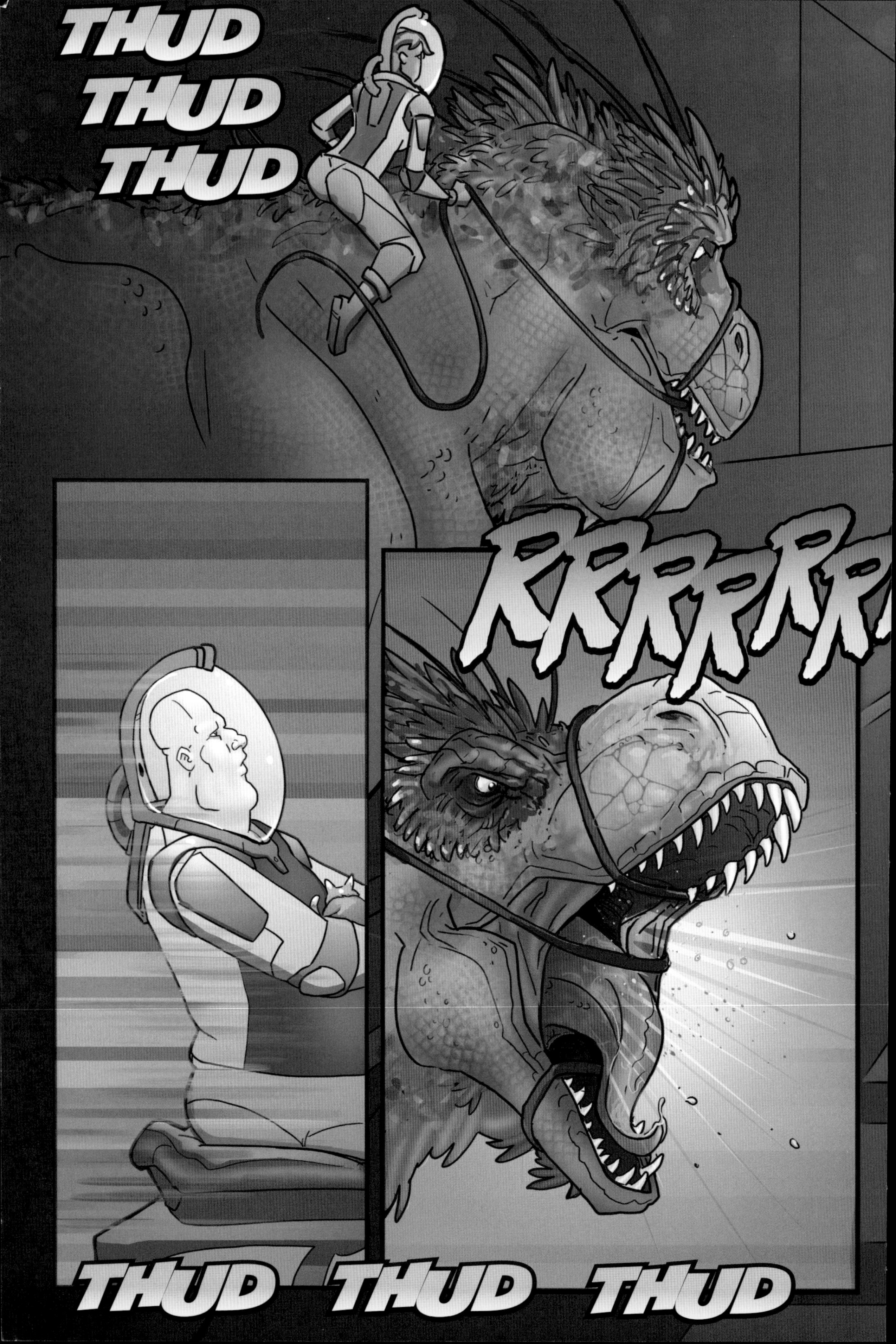
THUD
THUD
THUD
RRRRRRR
THUD THUD THUD

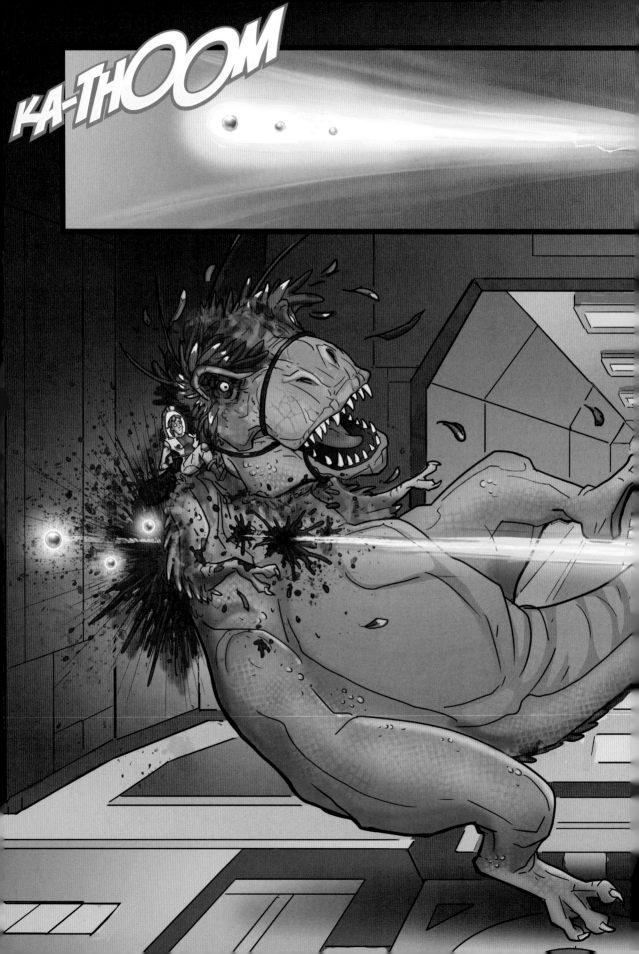

MUCH LATER . . .

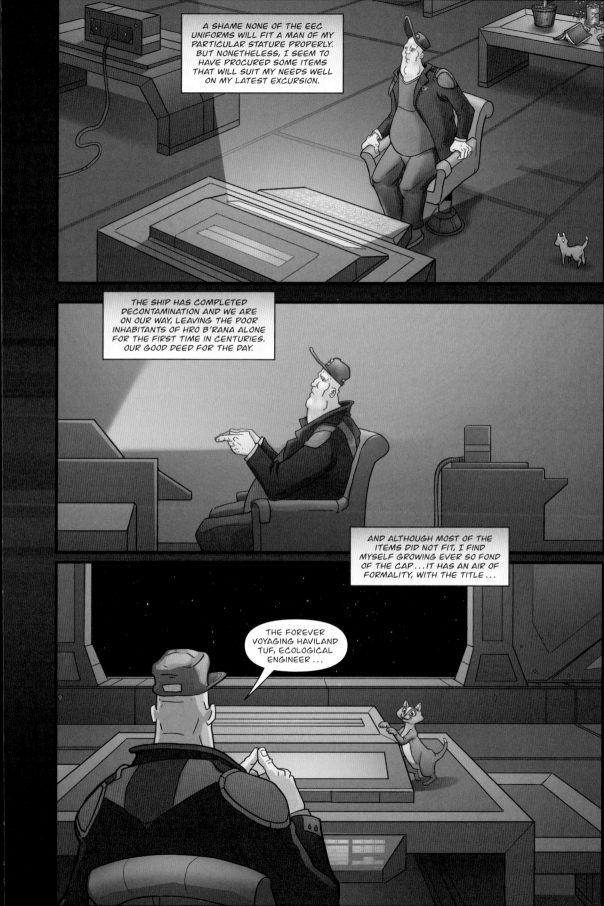

ABOUT THE ARTIST

RAYA GOLDEN GRADUATED FROM SAN FRANCISCO'S ACADEMY OF ART UNIVERSITY IN 2007 WHERE SHE FOCUSED ON TRADITIONAL AND DIGITAL ILLUSTRATION. SHE USES A VARIETY OF MEDIUMS TO BRING HER UNIQUE AND STYLIZED VISION INTO THE WORLD. SHE HAS MORE THAN A DECADE OF EXPERIENCE IN COMIC ART AND HER WORK HAS BEEN NOMINATED FOR A HUGO AWARD AND A NEBULA AWARD. SHE CURRENTLY RESIDES IN SANTA FE, NEW MEXICO, WITH HER CATS, MR. BOOGIE AND MISS BOOP, WHERE SHE LOVES TO PAINT AND DRAW WHILE A BARRAGE OF ULTRAGEEKY TV SHOWS AND MOVIES PLAY IN THE BACKGROUND.

ACKNOWLEDGMENTS

SPECIAL THANKS TO MY LINEWORK CONSULTANT SARAH FENTON, TO MY CO-MINIONS (ESPECIALLY SARAH AND SID) WHO SUPPORTED MY ABSENCE AT WORK, TO MY AMAZING TEAM AT TEN SPEED PRESS (KAITLIN KETCHUM AND CHLOE RAWLINS, I'M LOOKING AT YOU) FOR PUTTING UP WITH ALL MY WEIRDNESS, AND FINALLY, TO MY AUNTIE PARRIS WHO SOMEHOW MANAGED TO CONVINCE ME THAT I'M AS COOL AS SHE IS.

ABOUT THE AUTHOR

GEORGE R. R. MARTIN IS A NEW YORK TIMES BESTSELLING AUTHOR OF MANY NOVELS, SUCH AS *TUF VOYAGING*, *FEVRE DREAM*, *THE ARMAGEDDON RAG*, *DYING OF THE LIGHT*, AND THE ACCLAIMED SERIES *A SONG OF ICE AND FIRE*. THE *SONG OF ICE AND FIRE* SERIES INSPIRED THE HIGHLY INFLUENTIAL, AWARD-WINNING HBO TELEVISION SERIES *GAME OF THRONES* AND THE PREQUEL SERIES *HOUSE OF THE DRAGON*. AS A WRITER-PRODUCER, HE HAS WORKED ON *THE TWILIGHT ZONE* AND *BEAUTY AND THE BEAST*. HE LIVES WITH THE LOVELY PARRIS IN SANTA FE, NEW MEXICO, AND IS KEEPING BUSY.

SOCIAL MEDIA

GEORGERRMARTIN.COM

 @GRRMSPEAKING

 @GEORGERRMARTINOFFICIAL

RAYAGOLDEN.COM

 @RAYAGOLDEN

 @RAYAGOLDENILLUSTRATION

 @RAYAGOLDEN

HarperVoyager, an imprint of HarperCollinsPublishers Ltd
1 London Bridge Street, London, SE1 9GF

www.harpercollins.co.uk

HarperCollinsPublishers
Macken House, 39/40 Mayor Street Upper,
Dublin 1, D01 C9W8, Ireland

First published in Great Britain by HarperCollinsPublishers 2023
1

Text copyright © 2023 George R. R. Martin
Editor: Kaitlin Ketchum | Production editor: Sohayla Farman | Editorial assistant: Kausaur Fahimuddin
Art Director and interior designer: Chloe Rawlins | Cover Designer: Meggie Ramm
Adaptation, pencils, inks, and final colors: Raya Golden
Color assistance: Evan Evans (E2 Color Creations)
Letterer: Carlos M. Mangual
Production manager: Dan Myers
Copyeditor: Carol Burrell | Proofreader: Mikayla Butchart
Publicist: David Hawk | Marketer: Ashleigh Heaton

Typeface(s): Blambot's Jack Armstrong and Monotype's Posterama 2001

A catalogue record for this book is available from the British Library.

Trade Paperback ISBN: 978-0-00-865894-6

This is a graphic adaptation of 'The Plague Star' from TUF VOYAGING
by George R. R. Martin (Wake Forest, NC: Baen Books, 1986),
copyright © 1986 by George R. R. Martin.

First published in Great Britain in 1987 by Victor Gollancz Ltd.

Printed and bound in the U.K. by Bell & Bain Ltd.